INSECTS ON PARADE

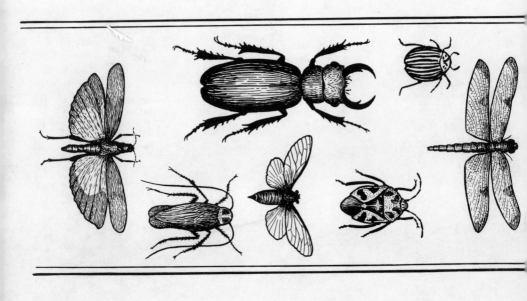

Insects on Parade

BY

CLARENCE J. HYLANDER

Drawings by the author

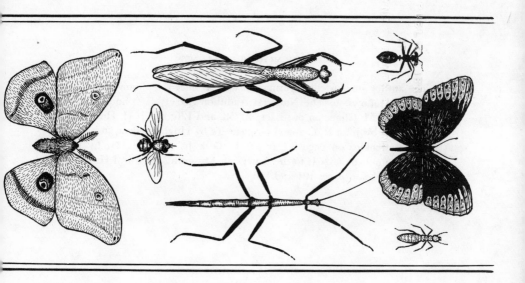

THE MACMILLAN COMPANY
NEW YORK

Library of Congress catalog card number: 57–7887

ACKNOWLEDGMENTS

The author acknowledges permission to reproduce the photographs in this book as follows: to The National Audubon Society for photographs by Lynwood M. Chace on pages 24, 40, 58, and 126; by H. H. Harrison on page xiv; by John R. Clawson on page 46; by Hugh Spencer on page 78; by Lee Jenkins on page 98; by N. E. Beck Jr. on page 131; by W. T. Davidson on page 164; to the American Museum of Natural History for photographs on pages 101 and 150.

Fifth Printing, 1967

PRINTED IN THE UNITED STATES OF AMERICA

CONTENTS

hawk moths. Tiger moths. Underwings
and their relatives. Moths with notorious
larvae: clothes moths, bagworm moths,
codling moth, tent caterpillar, inchworms,
gypsy moth.

True flies: house, blow, fruit, and horse
flies; gall midges; Tachina fly; mosquitoes.
Dragonflies and damselflies. Caddisflies.

Wasps: gall, cicada killer, sand, potter
and mud-dauber wasps; hornets and yel-
lowjackets. Bees: mining, leafcutting, and
carpenter bees; bumblebee; honeybee.
Ants: army, harvester, honey, carpenter,
Texas leafcutting, and slavemaking ants.
Termites.

FOREWORD

INSECTS ON PARADE. What a fantastic and fascinating procession such a parade would be! Imagine sitting in a grandstand seat and having magic glasses which would enlarge each insect to the size of a dog or a cat, perhaps even to that of a bear or an elephant. We will have to get comfortably seated, for it will take hours and hours for all the families and clans of the insects to pass in review. If only *one* individual of each kind of insect is in the parade and if each is allowed but *one* inch of space, the parade will stretch out for ten miles. There are 700,000 different kinds of insects.

Like all parades, this one has its workhorses and its labor crews, its acrobats and aerialists, its giants and dwarfs, its freaks and musicians, and most stunning of all, its beautiful and graceful performers.

A brightly colored array of beetles heads the procession. Here are metallic and iridescent tiger beetles, green and blue ground beetles, orange and black ladybird beetles, black and gold tortoise beetles, fearsome stag beetles and horned beetles. Following these land beetles comes a long line of bugs in infinite variety of shapes and sizes. Tiny and varicolored plant bugs, lace bugs proudly displaying their sculptured wings, stink bugs kept at a safe distance by the other paraders, for they are the skunks of the insect world.

Some bugs and beetles disport themselves in tanks of water hauled in the procession by sturdy worker ants, so they can display their aquatic skills. Long-legged water striders skate on the surface of the water. Water boatmen scull through the water with their oar-like limbs. Backswimmers, whose folded forewings form a nicely keeled boat, propel themselves on their backs with paddle-like limbs. More spirited movement is given the insect aquacade by the speedy diving beetles and the dancing whirligig beetles.

Like great formations of accompanying planes hover the numerous kinds of flies—tiny midges, larger and noisier horse flies and deer flies with a drone like speedy jet planes, metallic blue and green blow flies, and many other fruit and house flies. A familiar buzzing among these winged paraders tells of the presence of mosquitoes, also members of the fly contingent.

Instead of crawling or flying, the next group comes along with leaps and bounds. These are the members of the grasshopper brigade. Various kinds of grasshoppers and locusts move along with tremendous jumps on their powerful hind legs. Crickets and katydids follow for they too are part of the grasshopper clan. Most grotesque of all the paraders is the praying mantis whose devout appearance, with forelegs uplifted as in prayer, is not in keeping with its murderous habits. Here too comes the unusual walkingstick, like a twig endowed with life. Amid their more attractive relatives move the lowly roaches; they at least can be proud of an ancestry which goes back in prehistoric time farther than any other insects' in the parade.

Next in the procession is the large assemblage of ants, bees and wasps. Some are flying, some crawling, for not all have wings. In appearance most of them are not very unusual, either in color or in shape. However some of these are socially minded insects, proud of an achievement comparable to that of man in creating community life. Among themselves they number artisans and skilled farmers and mechanics, carrying on activities undreamed of by most of the other paraders.

Butterflies and moths add a dazzling splendor to the insect parade. Dainty and colorful aerial performers, they swoop and soar and wheel along the line of march. Some have wings as white as snow, others dark purple as the shadows of night; stripes and spots and silvery crescents adorn wings of a rainbow range of color, as swallowtails, monarchs, fritillaries and woodnymphs pass in review. Giant cecropia and polyphemus moths, and the dainty luna, are conspicuous among the many more sombre-colored moths.

Stationed at intervals along the ranks of the crawling, jumping, swimming and flying throng are the musicians who set the pace for the paraders. Grasshoppers produce a throbbing drumbeat by scraping their hind legs against their bodies. Crickets chirp on a merry note as they rub

their violin bows over their wingcases. Louder is the re-
sounding throbbing of the cicadas, musicians equipped
with built-in cymbals in their bodies. Katydids, by rubbing their front wings together, repeat over and over
again their familiar chant. Also along the line of march,
ready to light the way as darkness falls, are those beacons
of the insect realm, the fireflies and their glow-worm
young. The twinkling lights add a festive air to the
parade as the day ends.

You do not have to rely on imagination to witness
such a parade. Insects are all about us most of the year,
parading under our very noses. Entomologists—biologists
who study insects—tell us that the average backyard is
home for at least a thousand different kinds of insects, and
that one can find 15,000 different kinds within fifty miles
of a large city such as New York. One of the fascinations
of insect study is this easy availability of individuals for
observation. With keen eyes and a magnifying glass,
with patience and a willingness to sprawl close to the
earth, you can watch your own insect parade without
traveling far from home.

Once you have become acquainted with the names of
some of the paraders you will want to know more about
each one's habits. Why do they look the way they do?
What do they eat? How do they manage to get around in
the air, on the land, and under the water? Do they have
homes, and if so what are they like? The answers to
these and many other questions make a story far stranger
than fiction, but to answer all of them would take a
huge volume. Merely listing the names of all the different kinds of insects would require a book of 3300
pages! All we can do, in a few hundred pages, is to pro-

vide an intriguing glimpse into this incredible Lilliputian world. Perhaps the glimpse will whet your curiosity to learn more.

INSECTS ON PARADE can thus be used as a point of embarkation for your further thrilling adventures in a world of strange animals which often look like creatures from another planet, and into the absorbing literature which describes this insect world. When you have finished the last chapter of this book I know you will agree with me that insects are, to say the least, the most unusual members of the animal kingdom.

Clarence J. Hylander
Brooksville, Maine
November, 1956

The familiar grasshopper is a typical insect, with its head adorned with compound eyes and antennae, a segmented body, three pairs of legs, and wings.

CHAPTER ONE

MEET THE INSECTS

The animal kingdom is a fascinating and rewarding realm for exploration. It is ready to yield up its secrets whether we have a minute or a month to devote to it. It is at our doorsteps, along our highways, in our gardens and our woods, in the hidden retreats of our national parks. It offers such varied appeal that each of us can select what has the most interest to him. Rare is the person who has not at some time or other come face to face with a member of the realm without wondering what kind of animal he has encountered, what its name is, why it looks the way it does, what it is doing and why, how it defends itself and captures its food. These and a thousand other questions come to mind as we make the acquaintance of a wild animal.

Some of us strike up a friendship with mammals, look for them on our walks in the woods, keep them as pets, study their activities and behavior. Others are attracted to the birds, with their beauty of plumage and cheery songs. Fishermen become wise in the habits of fish, and want to know more about these water-dwellers than is necessary merely to catch them for food. Even the reptiles and amphibians have their devoted followers, strange as that may seem to bird-lovers and hunters.

All these animals have several things in common. They are relatively large animals, readily observed with the unaided eye. They are also built on a body plan similar to our own; they have an internal skeleton of bone, two pairs of limbs, two eyes, a brain which makes intelligent behavior possible.

These animals are not the only members of the wild-life community. We have omitted one very large group: the insects. To many people, watching insects has a great disadvantage; they are all small animals (our largest only six inches in wingspread), which require close observation, usually with a magnifying glass. We shall see later however that their small size is a great advantage to the insects themselves. They are often grotesque animals, making us uneasy as we look at their strange bodies; some look as if they had come from Mars, or another solar system. But it is this strange body plan, so different from ours, which makes them fascinating. Last but far from least, many insects interfere so much with our gardening and farming activities, or annoy us with their bites and stings, that we condemn the whole group for the misdeeds of the few. To those of us who have become acquainted with insects, however, they reveal an intriguing variety of color and body ornamentation, as well as many activities unknown in the world of mammals and birds.

What Is an Insect?

Every kind of animal, from a beetle to a grizzly bear, starts out its life with an inherited body plan and an ability to carry out activities designed to keep it alive. We say it is "adapted" to a particular environment and way of life. Keeping alive means being able to do a number of things, but of utmost importance is getting food. This involves sense organs, limbs, and muscles. These parts of the body, for most large animals, require a supporting framework which we call the skeleton.

Our familiar land animals—mammals, birds, reptiles—have specialized in an internal skeleton of bone. The axis of this framework is the backbone, or vertebral column, and as a result these animals are grouped together as *vertebrates*. Animals with backbones are so much like us in their development of sense organs, muscles, locomotor organs, and nervous systems that this seems a "natural" way to be constructed. But the vertebrate skeleton does not afford protection to the body; these animals have solved this problem by enveloping the softer inner organs in a skin covered with hair, feathers, or scales.

Another group of animals has progressed along the line of having the supporting framework on the outside of their bodies. These animals, lacking a backbone, are known as *invertebrates*. There are some simple invertebrates which have no skeleton at all, since they live in surroundings where a supporting framework seems unnecessary. Animals of this type are the earthworm and simple marine organisms like the jellyfish and sea anemone. Other invertebrates have an external skeleton in the form of a rigid limy shell; these include the clams and oysters. Such a shell is excellent protection but it is so cumbersome that the animal within is limited in its movements. A light but strong flexible shell would seem to be a satisfactory compromise between heavy armor and rapid movement. This has become the specialty of a third kind of invertebrate—the insect. Its outside skeleton is a marvelously light yet firm shell of chitin, arranged in segments to permit ease of movement. Insects

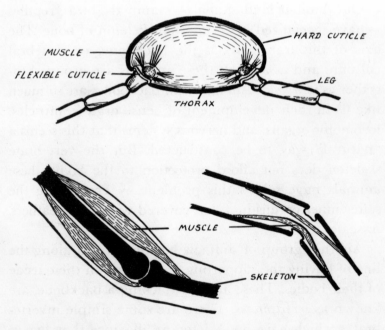

The skeleton of an insect is on the outside of the body; in the legs this skeleton surrounds the muscle, rather than forming an axis within the limb, as in mammals and man.

Insects and Their Relatives among the Arthropods

	Insects	Spiders	Millipedes	Centipedes	Crustaceans
Body Divisions	Head Thorax Abdomen	Cephalo-thorax Abdomen	Head Body	Head Body	Cephalo-thorax Abdomen
Number of Walking Legs	6	8	60 or more	30 or more	10
Number of Antennae	2	0	2	2	4
Method of Breathing	Tracheae	Tracheae	Tracheae	Tracheae	Gills
Types of Locomotion	Legs Wings	Legs	Legs	Legs	Legs
Habitat	Land, Air & Water	Land	Land	Land	Water (few on land)

therefore are invertebrates with an outside skeleton of chitin.

Locomotion is much easier for an animal with appendages; insects possess appendages which correspond to mammal limbs, and are equally effective for walking, crawling, jumping, digging, swimming, and flying. A marked difference between the mammal limb and the appendage of an insect lies in the relation of the skeleton to the muscles. In the mammal arm or leg, the skeleton forms a bony axis inside the limb, and the muscles are attached to the outer surface of the bones. In the insect leg, the skeleton surrounds the muscle as a chitinous shell or cuticle, and the muscles are anchored to its inner surface.

The segmented body, external skeleton, and jointed legs are characteristics of a large assemblage of invertebrates beside the insects. This group is known as the *Arthropoda,* a Greek term meaning "jointed feet." It also includes spiders, centipedes, millipedes, lobsters, and crabs. The accompanying table will help you tell the difference between these arthropods, some of which are often mistaken for insects. An important feature to look for is the number of walking legs. Insects have three pairs, spiders have four pairs, common crustaceans five pairs, and the centipede-millipede clan fifteen or more pairs.

A typical insect has two other characteristics. Its body is usually separated into three readily visible portions: a head, a thorax, and an abdomen. Each is separated by a deeply cut region, which is responsible for the origin of the word "insect," which is of Latin origin and

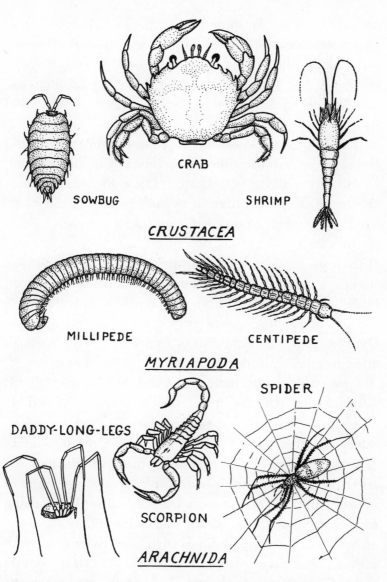

CRAB

SOWBUG

SHRIMP

CRUSTACEA

MILLIPEDE

CENTIPEDE

MYRIAPODA

SPIDER

DADDY-LONG-LEGS

SCORPION

ARACHNIDA

The Arthropoda constitute a large assemblage of invertebrates which includes, in addition to the insects, the Crustaceans, Myriapods, and Arachnids or spiders.

– 7 –

means "incised." In some insects this incised region may be as slender as a thread. In insects, unlike all other arthropods, the thorax may bear one or two pairs of wings. A few insects do not have wings; familiar examples of these are the worker caste of ants and termites.

Insects are a most successful group of animals, bearing the same relation to other invertebrates in this respect, as mammals do to vertebrates. Their success has been the result of a combination of biological factors. Their small size makes it possible for an insect to reach maturity in a very short time, measured in weeks or months, with a minimum food requirement. The small size makes it possible also for them to live in many places, especially as parasites, from which other larger animals are excluded. Insects are very prolific, a female often laying eggs by the hundreds or thousands in a season. In one summer, if all the offspring of a pair of flies survived, the parents would have 191,000,000,000,000,000,000 descendants! Insects have developed an incredible variety of efficient methods for getting food for themselves and their young. There is hardly a plant, animal, or any remains of plants and animals which does not serve as food for an insect. Finally, and perhaps of greatest importance, insects are very capable of taking care of themselves. In offense and defense they have few equals in animals many times their size. Even man, with all his scientific weapons, is at times powerless to overcome them. Some biologists think that insects are the only serious competitors in the entire animal world to threaten man's control of the earth.

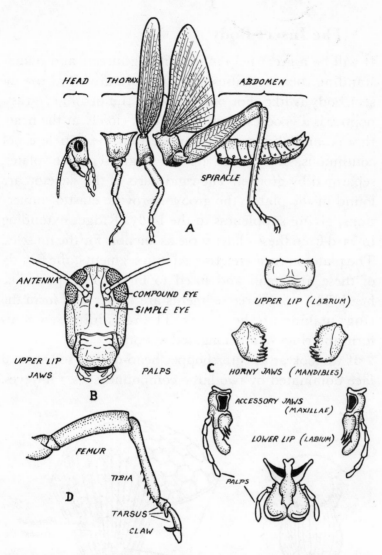

The body of a grasshopper is divided into a head, thorax and abdomen (A); a front view of the head (B) reveals eyes, antennae,
and various mouth parts; these mouth parts, when removed (C)
show specialization into lips, jaws, and sensory palps; the leg (D)
consists of flexible sections terminating in a claw.

The Insect Body

It will be a great help in identifying insects and understanding their activities if we can picture what the insect body is like. For our purposes the ordinary grasshopper is a good example. If we look closely at the head, thorax, and abdomen we can see that the cuticle is not continuous, but made up of small separate plates, separated by grooves. The rigid parts of the skeleton are found in the plates; the grooves provide elastic connections, giving suppleness to the body. Ridges extending inward from these plates serve as anchors for the muscles. The plates in turn are grouped into segments; the first six of these are small and fused to form the capsule-like head. The next three segments are larger and form the rings making up the thorax. The remaining segments form the rings of an elongated abdomen.

If we look at the grasshopper head-on, we see an oval face dominated by two large compound eyes. Our eyes,

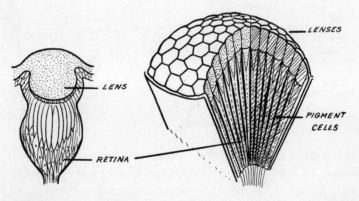

The ocellus, or simple eye, has a single lens; the larger compound eye (*right*) has many lenses.

– 10 –

and those of other vertebrates, consist of a single lens bringing an image to a sensitive retina. The compound eye on the other hand is a combination of thousands of small eyes, each with a lens and retina; each lens forms a facet of the compound eye. Such eyes are very sensitive to the slightest movement. We all know how difficult it is to swat a fly. Insects do not get as clear an image as we do, but a mosaic picture of the external world. In color vision, insects can see more of the ultraviolet end of the spectrum than we do, less of the red end. They also have three smaller eyes, or ocelli, between the compound eyes.

Most insects, like the grasshopper, have a pair of feelers, or antennae, arising between the eyes. These are important sense organs. Some have delicate hairs which pick up sound vibrations. Others have olfactory cells, making the antennae sense organs of smell. All antennae

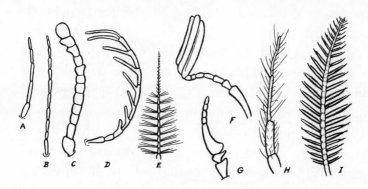

Antennae vary from simple filaments to branched or feathery structures, as shown by the dragonfly (A), various beetles (B, C, D), mosquito (E), June Beetle (F), horse fly (G), bug (H), and moth (I).

are sensitive to touch. If we watch insects closely we can see them cleaning their antennae carefully, for they depend upon them far more than they do on their eyes. The antennae of crickets are longer than their bodies, and those of moths are complex branched structures resembling small feathers.

Mouth parts of insects are far more complex than ours. These consist of an upper lip, or labrum, and a lower lip, or labium. Between the lips are two kinds of jaws: a pair of unsegmented horny jaws or mandibles, and a pair of segmented jaws known as maxillae. Insects get their food in two ways; by chewing and by sucking. In the chewing insects, of which the grasshopper is an example, the stout-toothed mandibles function as cutting and grinding organs. Unlike our jaws they move sidewise, like a pair of scissors, rather than up and down. With these tools insects are able to cut leaves, flowers, stems, and roots of plants. Crickets, mantids, termites, beetles, and wasps are a few kinds of insects with chewing mouth parts. They also occur in the larvae, or immature stages, of moths and butterflies. In the sucking insects, the mandibles and maxillae are sharp tools which can pierce like a hypodermic needle. The maxillae fit together to form a tube for sucking up blood or sap; biting flies have six such piercing structures. Most complicated of all is the proboscis of a moth or butterfly, which acts as a long hollow "tongue" to extract nectar from flowers.

A short flexible neck connects the head with the midsection of the grasshopper's thorax. All three of these segments bear appendages which function as legs, one pair to each segment. In a few adult insects and in some immature stages, one or more pairs of legs may be absent. Each leg consists of five jointed sections, the foot terminating in a pad or claw, or both. Adhesive pads make it possible for many insects to walk upside down on smooth surfaces like ceilings. Some legs are slender and long, as in the mosquitoes. Others are thick and muscular, such as the jumping legs of the grasshopper or the grasping legs of a mantid. Legs of water insects are flattened or hairy to increase their effectiveness as oars and paddles.

When two pairs of wings are present they occur on the last two segments of the thorax, one pair to each segment. Each wing is a paper-thin outgrowth of the body wall, forming the light yet strong structure necessary for flight. Insect wings are very thin, in cross section, consisting chiefly of cuticle, which forms the membranous surface, supported by a framework of veins. These veins are not part of the circulatory system and thus are perhaps unfortunately named. In adult insects the veins are reinforced tubes through which air circulates as part of

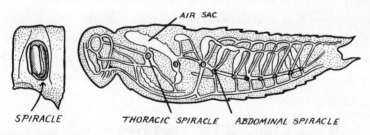

SPIRACLE   THORACIC SPIRACLE   ABDOMINAL SPIRACLE

The respiratory system of an insect consists of breathing pores or spiracles through which air enters and leaves a branching system of air-tubes or tracheae which carry air to every part of the body.

the respiratory system. Wings may be transparent or leathery, hairy or scaly; in many species they, like the head and thorax, are brilliantly colored.

The abdomen usually consists of ten segments. If we look closely at the abdomen of the grasshopper, we can see minute openings, one in each segment, along the sides; similar openings occur on some of the thoracic segments. These are breathing pores, or spiracles, and open into a system of tubes known as tracheae inside the body of the insect. The tracheae and spiracles form a unique and effective method of breathing. Air passes into these tubes, which branch into smaller channels carrying air to every part of the body. Finally they end in thin-walled cells through which oxygen and carbon dioxide can pass, in and out of the tissues. In mammals this gaseous exchange is one of the functions of the blood, which therefore is red, due to red corpuscles. Insect blood is greenish or yellowish, rarely red.

Also on the abdomen of the grasshopper we find an oval eardrum on each side of the first segment. Thus these insects hear with their abdomens. Other insects, such as the crickets, have their ears on their forelegs. The abdomen has no appendages except at the tip, where there may be a pair of clasping organs known as cerci. Projecting like a long spine from the end of the abdomen of many female insects is the ovipositor, a structure used in laying eggs.

What Kinds of Insects Live in the United States?

The tremendous numbers of insect species makes it seem hopeless for a beginner to identify them. Entomologists estimate that there are at least 700,000 different kinds of insects in the world. Like the national budget, or the distances to the stars, such a large figure is hard to comprehend. Other kinds of animals, totaling only 300,000 altogether, number less than half the insect species. Put in another way, insects far exceed the 100,000 kinds of vertebrates, or the 20,000 species of mammals. Thus insects predominate in any kind of habitat where we find wild life; they are common in woods, fields, and around our homes. In temperate parts of the United States they go into hiding in the winter, but in the other months they can be found everywhere.

All of these species are not found in the United States; the insect population of our country is only about 10% of the world total. In many ways we can be thankful for this, as we will see when we consider the relations of insects to man. Even this number is not found in any one state; for the distribution depends upon climate, available food, kind of land surface, and enemies. Few states have made a complete census of their insect life, but based on those that have we can expect to find about 10,000 to 15,000 species in the average state: enough to keep a young naturalist well occupied!

Beside the great number of species, the number of individuals in each species staggers the imagination, running into millions and billions. Ant hills may contain 100,000 tenants. Honeybees are packed 50,000 to 80,000 in a hive. In the United States termite nests with a quarter of a million inhabitants are small compared with the 3,000,000 per colony in South America. Four and a half million insects have been found per acre in the upper six inches of soil in North Carolina. But even these fantastic numbers mean little when compared with the abnormally high populations which occur at times when insect hordes appear, under favorable living and family-raising conditions. A locust swarm which appeared in the last century over Nebraska contained an estimated 124,000,000,000 individuals. Smaller swarms of cicadas, tent caterpillars and army ants periodically sweep over the fields and woods. Mankind, for all his intelligence and much greater size, often is powerless against the multitudes of these tiny animals.

The insect world, however, becomes less confusing when we look at it through the eyes of the entomologists who have attempted to classify these thousands of species into large groups, or orders, each with its own distinctive features by which it can be recognized even by the untrained naturalist. A familiarity with the orders most commonly encountered makes it easier to recognize the various members of our insect parade.

The largest order is that of the beetles, of which there are 26,000 species in the United States; it is known as the *Coleoptera,* a scientific name meaning "sheath-wings" and referring to their most characteristic feature. Beetles have two pairs of wings, but the forewings are useless for flight, being leathery and hard. These meet in a straight line along the back of the insect when at rest, forming a protective covering for the membranous flying wings beneath. Many beetles are brightly colored, others are ornamented with horns and spines; the majority are small insects, only a few inches in length. All beetles have chewing mouth parts. Some are herbivorous, feeding on leaves and other juicy plant tissues, or on wood.

Others are carnivorous and prey on fellow insects. Some are scavengers, eating dead animals and their waste products. Familiar beetles include such garden pests as the Japanese Beetle and the Colorado Potato Beetle, and such curious members as the click beetles, scarab beetles, and the stag beetles.

The second largest order in the United States is that of the flies, or *Diptera,* with some 16,000 species. Here again the scientific name refers to the chief recognition feature of the order for it means "two wings." These are the only insects which normally have but one pair of wings; these are the forewings, the hindwings being replaced by stabilizers, or balancing organs. The single pair of wings are highly effective for flight, however, as we find when we learn that flies are among the fastest-flying insects. Many other insects are popularly known as "flies"—dragonflies, caddisflies, and fireflies—but these have two pairs of wings, and belong to other orders. Flies are scavengers, but in some species also have sucking mouth parts which make them annoying and dangerous because of their ability to feed on plant sap or blood. The mosquito is a special kind of fly.

A competitor for second place is the *Hymenoptera,* the order which includes the ants, wasps, and bees. Some 14,000 species have been described for the United States. The scientific name, meaning "membrane wings" refers to the cellophane-like texture of the wings, of which there are two pairs, with the forewings the larger. The body is usually noticeably constricted between the thorax and the abdomen. In the ants, the workers, which are the insects we usually see, are wingless. Many of the

Hymenoptera are solitary insects, living as individuals; but others are socially inclined and have developed a type of community life which has long been the wonder of the animal kingdom. From the human viewpoint social insects are a beneficial group, aiding in pollinating plants, destroying injurious insects, and providing honey.

Another large group is that of the *Lepidoptera,* the order which includes the moths and butterflies. The name means "scale wings" and refers to the tiny dust-like scales which cover the thin wings like shingles on a roof, and which rub off easily when the insects are handled. Some 10,000 species occur in the United States. To many people the thought of an insect automatically conjures up the picture of a moth or butterfly. In fact we are likely to think of an entomologist as one who spends his time chasing butterflies with a net. Adult Lepidoptera are conspicuous and attractively colored insects. But they are the Dr. Jekyll and Mr. Hyde of the animal world. When full grown, they are the picture of charm and innocence, flitting in a harmless fashion from flower to flower. But their young, as caterpillars and cutworms, are often mischievous and destructive, as well as forbidding in appearance. The cutworms found in sod and earth are the immature stages of moths and other insects.

Many insects are called "bugs" by the average person, but to an entomologist a bug means a member of the order *Hemiptera,* with some 8000 species in this country. The name means "half wing" and refers to a feature of a large group of bugs; of the two pairs of wings, the forewing is partly membranous, partly thickened and leathery at the base. The forewings, being longer than the hindwings, protect the latter as well as the body. At rest these wings are held flat over the abdomen, with the tips overlapping. All bugs have piercing or sucking mouth parts; some use these in feeding on plant juices, others are carnivorous and feed on fellow insects. This order includes a large number of aquatic species: water striders, backswimmers, water boatmen. Land-dwellers, often found on stems, leaves, and flowers of plants number among them such familiar bugs as squash bugs, stink bugs, treehoppers, aphids, and scale insects. The cidada is also in this assemblage.

The remaining orders number much fewer species. Grasshoppers, also known as locusts, make up most of the order *Orthoptera;* some of the species in this order are winged, and these have a front pair of thickened or leathery wings, and membranous hindwings which can fold fanwise against the body. Some intriguing insects belong to this order: the musically inclined crickets and katydids, the grotesque praying mantis, and the wingless walking stick.

Termites belong to the order *Isoptera.* Two pairs of wings, of equal size, are found on the kings and queens; the workers and soldiers are wingless. Termites are often confused with ants, but we shall see later that an observant person can readily distinguish between them. Another small order is that of the *Odonata,* large insects with two pairs of narrow wings and an extremely long abdomen; these are the dragonflies and damselflies. Caddisflies belong to the order *Trichoptera,* which are especially distinguished by their two pairs of hairy wings and by the unusual portable homes that the larvae construct as they spend their youthful lives in the water.

The *Neuoptera,* whose two pairs of wings have a network of fine criss-crossing veins, are not very familiar as adults, but their larvae, the hellgrammites and antlions, are interesting members of the insect world. Adults are known as dobsonflies; the males have huge mandibles which project beyond the head, and are almost as long as the antennae. Females lay their eggs on stones and twigs near the water; the newly hatched larvae, known as hellgrammites, live beneath stones in shallow streams. Hellgrammites are often used by fishermen as live bait. The adults of antlions are large insects resembling damselflies; the larvae are the "antlions" which dig conical pits in sandy or powdery soil as traps in which to catch their meals. The antlion lies partly buried at the bottom, with its powerful jaws barely visible. When a luckless insect falls down the side of the pit, it slides into the waiting mouth of the antlion and is immediately paralyzed by an injection of anesthetic.

How Can We Identify Insects

Professional entomologists identify an unknown insect by use of a device known as a key. This is a word-map noting certain identification characters; the corresponding features of the insect under consideration are compared to those on the key. Any insect mentioned in the key whose description does not match the insect whose identity is being established is disregarded as a possible candidate. With the elimination, one after another, of all those which are not like the insect being studied, there remains only one—the answer to the insect's true identity. Such keys are used also by other field biologists in identifying flowers, trees, birds, and mammals. Insect keys are very complicated and require a knowledge of details in the insect's life history and in easily over-looked features of wing venation and mouth parts. Field guides mentioned in the Afterword of this book include such keys for various orders.

If you are sure that the animal you have collected is an insect, you should first look for the presence or ab-sence of wings. If wings are absent, the insect most likely is a worker among the ants or termites, a walking stick, a flea, or a bed bug. All other insects have wings, with such few exceptions that they need not be men-tioned at this time.

If your specimen has wings, you should notice whether it has one pair of wings, or two pairs. If one pair is pres-ent, the insect is one of the flies, midges, or mosquitoes. If there are two pairs of wings, identification is not so easy, since this is a characteristic of all remaining in-sects. Our attention now must center on special wing features. Is the front pair entirely horny or leathery, a cover for the membranous hindwings? Is the front pair half membranous, half leathery? Are both pairs mem-branous and gauze-like? Are the wings covered with minute scales?

Presence of hard front wings identifies the insect as a beetle. Various secondary features will now help you. Is the insect aquatic or land-dwelling? If the former, it is either a diving beetle or a whirligig beetle. If land-dwelling, does the head terminate in a snout? If so, the insect is a snout beetle or weevil. If not, it may belong to one of many families. The firefly group has a luminous abdomen; the scarab beetles have peculiar antennae with leaf-like plates at the tip; the stag beetles have large mandibles. Color, shape of body, feeding habits are helpful in identifying the multitude of beetles.

Presence of leathery or parchment-like forewings, and mouthparts adapted for chewing, places the insect in the grasshopper clan. Those with hindlegs enlarged for jumping are the grasshoppers and locusts if the antennae are shorter than the body, crickets and katydids if the antennae are longer than the body. If the front legs are enlarged, the insect is a mantid.

The large thin scaly wings of moths and butterflies make identification of the members of that order easy; very few of these can be confused with any other insect group. Likewise the long abdomen of the damselfly and dragonfly is typical, and a useful recognition feature. Most wasps, bees, and ants are readily recognized as such. Professionals as well as beginners find it difficult to identify the various bugs; most helpful will be reference to illustrations in field guides.

Now we know a little about what an insect is, how it resembles some other animals and differs from still others. We can also picture what a typical insect looks like, even though most of them are so small that perhaps we have not taken such a careful look at them before. A sort of panoramic view of the insect world has given us a general idea of the variety of body shapes and habits of each group in our insect parade, and of the classification made possible by differing characteristics. Before becoming better acquainted with some of these groups, let us continue our exploration of the insect world by finding out how insects live; their methods of locomotion; their feeding habits; and their peculiar life cycle known as metamorphosis.

Head-on view of a Water Boatman

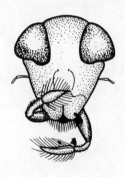

A young dragonfly has just hatched from the nymph case seen at lower left; an older dragonfly suns its wings at the upper right.

CHAPTER TWO

HOW INSECTS LIVE

Being able to recognize an insect by name is only the first step in exploring the insect world. Insects are restless animals, always doing something; so there is no monotony to insect-watching. Observing their behavior, to see how they live, has become a lifetime hobby of many naturalists. Some of these, like the French entomologist Jean Henri Fabre, have left us priceless accounts based on firsthand experiences in watching these little animals at their daily round of activities.

Insects reveal a remarkable variety of adaptations for moving about in and under the ground, in the water, and in the air. Their eating habits show an almost endless variety of adaptations; insects have mouth parts suited to eating practically anything on the earth's surface with nourishment in it, even wood. The family life of insects is fascinating: the role played by the mother in laying eggs, protecting them against vicissitudes of the environment, furnishing them with food available when they hatch, even feeding the young before they can eat by themselves. By far the most interesting activity to watch is the development of the newly hatched young into adults through the stages of metamorphosis. If time permitted, we could also tell of the construction of homes; detection of odors which we as humans cannot smell, and of sounds we cannot hear; offensive and defensive weapons and tactics; protection by form and color against enemies; agricultural practices similar to our dairying and farming activities.

Insect Locomotion

The six legs with which the majority of insects are provided furnish ample means for crawling, walking, and climbing. By their help insects are able to overcome obstructions in their path and scurry at a relatively rapid

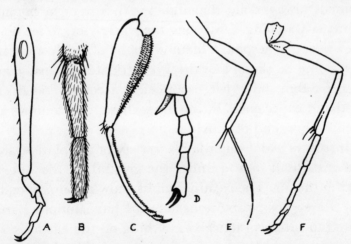

Insect legs serve a variety of functions and thus take on a variety of shapes, as seen in the katydid (A), water strider (B), water bug (C), diving beetle (D), gnat (E), and wasp (F).

speed over the ground. Insect legs may seem frail and brittle, but they are suprisingly sturdy, and easily able to support the light-weight bodies. Efficient muscles enable insects to drag incredibly heavy loads; we have all seen a tiny ant pulling and pushing the body of a dead insect many times its own size. Because of powerful muscles in their oversized hindlegs, grasshoppers and crickets are record-breaking high jumpers in the animal world. The legs are often armed with spines, as in the mantids, to give added purchase in grasping prey. In the honeybee, the legs are modified to use as special baskets for carrying materials. Hairy legs and feet give water striders their unusual ability to walk on the water.

Insect legs are also modified for use in special environments. The short, spade-like legs of the mole cricket assist this insect in digging through the ground. The legs of aquatic insects are flattened or edged with hairs to give greater surface. Diving beetles, water bugs, and backswimmers have such paddle-like legs.

Wings are a characteristic of most adult insects. In fact, if we look at a collection of mounted insects we see very little else; the wings are the most conspicuous part of their bodies, useful in identifying each species. Insects cannot fly as fast as birds, but they can maneuver better. Dragonflies, the most agile of insect fliers, can go forward and backward, remain poised in midair, or dart away faster than the eye can see. The botfly is the speediest insect in the air, with recorded speeds of 40 to 50 miles per hour. Hawk moths and wasps can "cruise" at 30 miles an hour. Flying insects can also cover great distances. Some butterflies migrate for a thousand miles, and locusts have become an international problem because of their dispersal flights over miles of land and sea.

The insect wing is a marvel of lightness and aeronautical design. Thin as cellophane, supported by a light but rigid framework of veins, insect wings are capable of beating at unbelievable speeds. Each wing is attached to the upper part of the thorax in such a way that the contraction of muscles within the thorax brings about the up and down strokes. The wing is elevated when the top of the thorax is pulled downward by muscles extending crosswise of the body; it is lowered when other muscles, running lengthwise within the thorax, contract. The flight of butterflies and moths is fluttery and leisurely, their broad wings making as few as six strokes per minute. Insects with smaller wings have a faster wing-beat. Bumblebee wings beat 200 times per second, small flies have a wing-beat as high as 350 strokes per second. In the fruit fly, *Drosophila,* the tiny wings move up and down at the rate of 13,000 strokes per minute!

Insect Feeding Habits

As we become familiar with different large groups of animals, such as birds and mammals, we discover that they have three types of feeding habits. Some species are

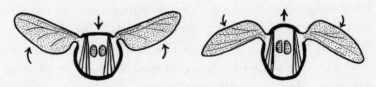

An insect wing is raised when the top of the thorax is pulled downward by special muscles (*left*); the downbeat of the wing occurs when the thorax moves upward as a result of contraction of other muscles (*right*).

herbivorous, feeding on plants and plant products. Others are *carnivorous,* eating whole animals or parts of their bodies. A few are *omnivorous,* less fussy in their tastes and ready to eat anything, plant or animal. Among familiar animals, a cow is a typical herbivor, a cat is a carnivor, and we ourselves are omnivors. Omnivorous animals are less highly specialized in their teeth and other mouth parts. Very few insects are omnivorous except the house-infesting pests, like roaches, and some aquatic bugs which feed on both water plants and water-dwelling animals. But the great majority of insects are either herbivorous or carnivorous. Such animals which concentrate on a particular kind of food usually have special adaptations for obtaining and digesting only that one kind of food.

The mouth parts of insects lend themselves well to modification as ingenious tools for cutting, chewing, and macerating tissues of plants, whether they be soft as a succulent leaf or hard as nuts or wood. They also can become spears for piercing plant bodies and syringes for sucking liquids. Needle-sharp mouth parts can become lethal weapons in those insects which suck blood. Hollow tongues perform the service of suction pumps, pulling nectar from the depths of flowers; hollow "hypodermic needles" can inject paralyzing doses of anesthetic into insect prey.

Entire orders of insects depend upon plants as food. Most familiar are the nectar-loving moths and butterflies, and their foliage-consuming larvae, the caterpillars. But plant feeders occur also among the grasshoppers and crickets, the beetles and the bugs. Many of these have a restricted menu, confining their feeding to a particular species of plant. In fact it is often easy to find a certain insect whose food habits you know, by locating the plant on which it feeds. Insects select such plants by the chemical odor of special compounds found only in certain families of plants. The pungent odor of the cabbage family attracts many insects, as does the foliage of cherry trees and the sap of the milkweeds. Caterpillars of cabbage butterflies eat no other kind of plant, and will die of starvation rather than move to another kind of food. Thus the mother Cabbage Butterfly instinctively lays her eggs only on cabbage plants. The same discrimination is true of the Colorado Potato Beetle, with its fondness for wild and cultivated members of the nightshade family, to which the potato belongs. The Mexican Bean Beetle concentrates on plants in the pea and bean family. This concentration on a certain kind of food is

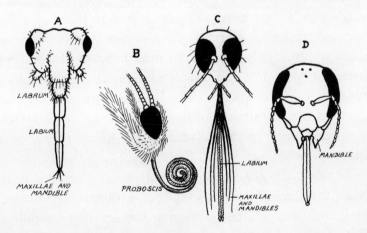

Some insect mouth parts are adapted for piercing and sucking as in bugs (A) and mosquitoes (C); others for siphoning liquids as in butterflies (B); others for lapping as in bees (D).

one reason for the extensive damage done by crop and garden pests. Man devotes acres to only one kind of plant; when the insect which feeds on this plant finds food in such easy abundance, it thrives and reproduces in numbers not possible in nature, where plants of one species are not found so profusely in one spot. In searching out its special food, the plant-feeding insect follows purely instinctive behavior; intelligence plays no part in its actions.

Every portion of a plant is food to some insect. Before the seed falls to the ground, it may have within it many eggs or immature stages of bugs or moths. If it germinates, the seedling is likely to be cut down by hungry insects and their young waiting in the earth for just such a feast. The white grubs of the common June Beetle are plant feeders of this type. The seedlings which grow to maturity and produce leaves provide a real banquet for our insect neighbors. When too many leaves are removed, the plant weakens and dies, for the foliage of a plant manufactures the food needed for its growth. Thus when grasshoppers and locusts, blister beetles and weevils, webworms and tent caterpillars descend upon it, the very life of the plant is threatened. Plants are weakened and killed by the sap-sucking insects, which insert their mouth parts in the leaves and stems and steal the vital plant sap. Their sucking mouth parts also spread virus diseases from plant to plant, often doing even more damage in this way than by stealing the plant juices. Stink bugs, chinch bugs, aphids, and scale insects are but a few of these plant-feeders. Other insects attack the ripening fruit. Even wood, not attractive as food to larger animals, is eaten by termites.

Carnivorous insects are typified by the dragonflies and flies. These flesh-eaters turn their hungry mouths on their fellow insects, partly because these animals are available, partly because they are not too large to attack with safety. Some of the aquatic bugs and beetles do tackle large prey, catching and eating tadpoles and small fish, but most insect-eaters depend upon more numerous and defenseless plant-feeders. When insects eat injurious crop pests, they unknowingly become our allies. The Lady Beetle is such a carnivorous insect, preying on aphids and scale insects. Strangely enough, the larvae of many of the carnivorous species are more bloodthirsty than their parents; few animals, ounce for ounce, are as ferocious as water tigers or antlions.

The digestive system of an insect differs in a few interesting ways from that of mammals. The mouth of the insect opens into a pharynx which, in the species with sucking mouth parts, has a particularly muscular wall. Insects, like other animals, produce enzymes which digest their food. Some species, however, have evolved the unique habit of injecting enzymes into the food before it

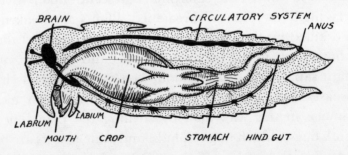

The digestive system of an insect consists of mouth, crop, stomach and hindgut; above it is the circulatory system, below it the nerve cord.

enters the digestive system. Thus only predigested food is taken in. The saliva of the blood-sucking mosquito contains a substance which prevents blood-clotting. This is injected when a mosquito bites; as a result the blood taken into the digestive tract does not coagulate and obstruct the food channels.

Food passes from the pharynx through a narrow gullet which extends into the thorax. Here the digestive system enlarges to form a crop, which in most insects is an elastic-walled chamber where digestion begins, but where food can also be temporarily stored. Mother insects regurgitate food from the crop in feeding their young. Honeybees carry nectar in their crops, while transporting it from flowers to storage cells in the hive; while in the crop the nectar is partly digested and begins its transformation into honey.

In the abdomen, the food tube becomes a midgut and a hindgut, where digestion of food is completed and residues prepared for excretion. Numerous kinds of enzymes act on the great variety of foods eaten by insects, ranging from plant sugars to wool fabrics. In the hindgut water is extracted from the food remnants, and excess water is filtered out in the form of honeydew by several kinds of sap-sucking insects. These exuded droplets of sugary solution are eaten by other insects, especially the ants, which use the aphids producing honeydew as man does dairy cattle. In termites the hindgut possesses colonies of Protozoa which digest wood.

Insects and Their Young

The insect world is dominated by the mother who plays the chief role in producing the family. Even in the social insects, such as the bees and the ants, the father is usually only a bystander in family activities and community affairs. In the solitary insects, where each individual lives by itself, the mother rarely is alive when her offspring are born. Thus she exerts unusual efforts in carefully selecting sites for laying her eggs, providing them with ample stores of food, and protecting them in nests.

Most insects develop from tiny eggs which hatch after they are laid; in only a very few species do the eggs develop within the mother so that the young insect is born alive. A few species, like the cricket, lays single eggs in the ground. Most insect mothers lay fifty to a hundred eggs, the most ambitious mothers being those among bees and termites where a million eggs may be laid in a lifetime. Some eggs are flattened and disc-shaped, others are round or hemispherical, still others are cylindrical and look like little barrels. Insect eggs are usually greenish or yellowish but some are brightly colored. Each egg is protected by a shell which may be smooth, ridged, or ornamented with spines. The egg masses are often laid in symmetrical bands and rows; eggs of moths look like carefully laid tiles encircling twigs. A number of insect mothers coat their egg masses with a shellac-like substance, cover them with hairy blankets, or envelop them in papery covers. The egg masses of the Praying Mantis, for example, form a braided parchment-like mass deposited on twigs of shrubs and trees.

One of the wonders of the insect world is the care with which the mother insect provisions the birthplace of her offspring. Insects with aquatic stages in their life history lay their eggs on plants or other objects in or near the water. Thus when the eggs hatch the gill-breathing youngsters find the right environment in which to develop. The gall-producing insects lay their eggs inside plants, first piercing a hole with their ovipositor and then laying the eggs deep within the plant tissues.**1423993**

Few mothers in the animal kingdom reveal the instinctive foresight of the Yucca Moth in carrying out her maternal duties. The Yucca, also called Spanish bayonet, is a shrubby plant of the Southwest, bearing huge clusters of lily-like flowers. It depends for pollination entirely upon the Yucca Moth, and the Yucca Moth's young can develop only in the heart of the Yucca blossom. The moth unerringly seeks out the blossom which is ready to be pollinated, stabs a deep hole with her ovipositor in the pistil and in it lays four or five eggs, next to the tiny ovules which will become seeds. When the moth eggs hatch, the larvae depend upon the seeds for food. However, no seeds will form unless the flower is pollinated. To be sure this happens, the moth mounts a stamen, scrapes off some pollen, carries it to the top of the pistil in which she has laid her eggs, and packs it down firmly. The strangest aspect of this behavior is that the moth takes neither pollen nor nectar as a reward for her work. Since each larva will eat only about twenty seeds, and the Yucca blossom is capable of producing ten times this number, enough seeds are left over to perpetuate the plant. What better cooperation between plant and animal could exist?

There are many examples of carnivorous insects which

lay their eggs in the bodies of other insects, so that when the eggs hatch they will have at hand an ample supply of fresh meat. Inhuman as this habit may seem to us, from the insect's point of view it is the best way in which to start out a young life. Comparable to the story of the Yucca Moth is that of the little Pyrgota Fly. We have all seen clumsy June bugs congregating around street lights on summer evenings. Among them may be a fast-flying little Pyrgota, looking for a place to lay her eggs. Suddenly she dives down onto a June bug, jabs her ovipositor into the vulnerable spot on the top of the back, while the bug's wings are spread in flight. In that second she has laid an egg in the body of her victim. The bug drops to the ground, but soon recovers and flies with its companions. Within a few days the egg hatches, and the larva begins to feed on the body fluids in the bug's body. As the larva grows stronger, the June bug grows weaker. In about ten days the larva begins to eat the muscles of its host, which soon results in death of the June bug. The larva now wastes no time in completely devouring the rest of the bug's body, leaving only an empty shell.

Some insects lay their eggs in carefully prepared nests, stocked with provisions. A large black-and-yellow wasp known as the Horse Guard patrols the backs of horses in search of her choice food—horse flies. The horse seems to know that the buzzing wasp is a friend, and stands motionless while she hovers around. Horse Guard wasps do not want the flies for themselves; they feed on nectar or honeydew. The flies are for the unborn young. The mother has previously dug a small nest in the soil—a tunnel ending in a nursery room where she has laid a single egg. The telltale pile of excavated material is carefully spread over the entrance to leave no sign of the nest. In two days the egg hatches; at this time the Horse Guard begins bringing in flies, which she has captured on the wing, by stinging them to death or merely paralyzing them. Carrying each fly to her nest she scrapes the sand away from the entrance and places the meal before her hungry youngster. Then she leaves, carefully hiding the entrance again. This is repeated again and again, the fresh flies keeping the developing larva well fed. As many as fifty flies will be needed to bring a young Horse Guard wasp to maturity.

Such behavior is duplicated by many other insects in various orders. Wasps are especially adept at this type of mother instinct, some laying their eggs on the backs of caterpillars, others puncturing their bodies and laying the eggs in the body tissues. One kind of hornet attacks cicadas and carries the entire insect, in a paralyzed state, to her nest; she lays her egg in the body of the living but unconscious cicada and thus provides her young, when hatched, with fresh meat. It is evident that such parasitic insects are of great value to man in reducing the number of injurious, plant-feeding species.

Metamorphosis

When the insect egg hatches, the newly born individual is very much on its own. Its first instinctive act is to reach out for food, and since the mother has anticipated this need, the young insect does not have far to go. Its appetite is tremendous, and growth begins at once. This means that the increasing size of the body creates a real problem. The outside skeleton of an invertebrate is excellent for protection and support but it is rigid and thus does not allow for increase in size during growth. Such an outside covering can be let out in the seams a little, as a growing boy's clothes can be altered. But this has its limits; a new suit is soon necessary. The growing insect gets a series of new suits by shedding the old small skin for a new and slightly larger one; the process is known as molting. An insect may molt from four to twelve times, but usually five to eight molts are sufficient to accommodate its growth. Before losing the old protective coat, a new one is formed beneath. At the right time a special molting fluid forms between the two layers and then the old outer covering is sloughed off. The cast-off skins of insects can often be found on twigs and rocks, split up the back where the animal crawled out of its old suit. The cast is often an exact replica of the entire insect.

During these molts the insect grows larger and larger, but also changes its form. These changes during development from the newly hatched young to the adult make up a process called metamorphosis. Insects exhibit two kinds of metamorphosis. In one called *simple metamorphosis,* the youngsters are much like their parents except for their smaller size, and change into the adult with no intervening resting stage. In such forms, if the adults are winged, the wings do not appear in the early stages. Simple metamorphosis occurs in the grasshopper clan, among dragonflies and damselflies, termites, and many bugs. In the other type, called *complete metamor-*

phosis, the young stages differ from the adult so greatly that they look like entirely different animals. Many are worm-like, and certainly give no indication of what their appearance will be when grown-up. Complete metamorphosis is typical of the moths and butterflies; the beetles; the wasps, bees, and ants; and the flies.

In simple metamorphosis, the young are called nymphs. If the parent has compound eyes, the nymphs also possess them. If the parents are winged, the nymph stages have budlike swellings which will later become the wings. The greatest difference between young nymphs and adults is found in the dragonflies, damselflies, and mayflies where the nymphs are aquatic. Structures for breathing in the water must be modified from the air-breathing tracheae found in the adults. Nymphs of dragonflies breathe by

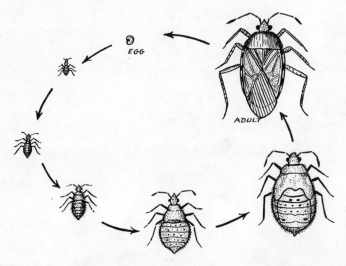

In simple metamorphosis the young, called nymphs, are much like their parents except for size and absence of wings. The grass bug has such a simple metamorphosis.

gills inside their bodies, those of damselflies by leaflike appendages extending behind the abdomen. Mayfly nymphs are elaborate-looking insects, with leaflike gills sprouting from the sides of each segment of the abdo-

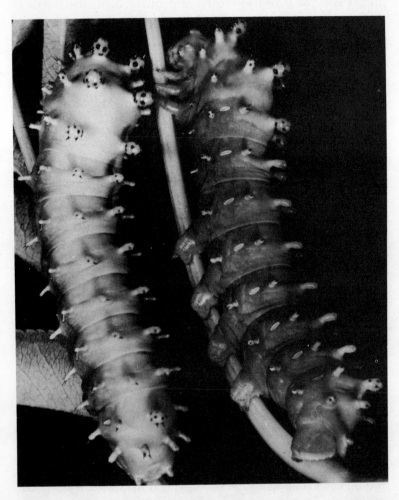

The worm-like caterpillar stage in complete metamorphosis seems far removed from the winged moth or butterfly. This Cecropia caterpillar is grotesquely armed with knobs and spines.

men. In the land-dwelling grasshopper clan, the succeeding series of nymphs look like miniature adults and live
the same sort of terrestrial life, but are unable to fly.

The changes taking place during complete metamorphosis have always fascinated observers of nature. The
worm-like crawling caterpillar transforming itself into a
resting stage or pupa and emerging as a winged moth or
butterfly is a miracle of growth. We can echo the words
of two pioneer entomologists who wrote, over a century
ago, that:

"Were a naturalist to announce to the world the discovery of an animal which first existed in the form of a
serpent; which then penetrated into the earth, and

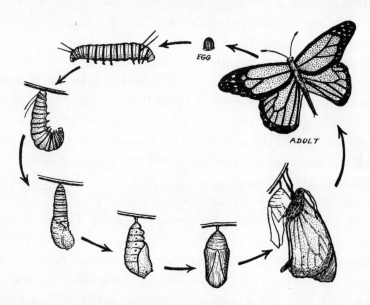

In complete metamorphosis the egg develops into a larval stage
which in turn becomes a pupa or resting stage in a chrysalis, and
from this the winged adult emerges. The Monarch butterfly is a
familiar insect undergoing complete metamorphosis.

– 41 –

weaving a shroud of pure silk of the finest texture, contracted itself within this covering into a body without external mouth or limbs, and resembling, more than anything else, an Egyptian mummy; and which, lastly after remaining in this state without food and without motion . . . should at the end of that period burst its silken cerements, struggle through its earthly covering and start into day a winged bird—what think you would be the sensation excited by this strange piece of intelligence?"

The young in those insects showing a complete metamorphosis differ markedly from their parents in appearance, and often in habits also. The first worm-like stages are called larvae, and correspond to the nymph stage in insects with incomplete metamorphosis. A larva lacks compound eyes, may or may not have legs, and does not develop wings. Its body is usually elongated and cylindrical, but with the segments as found in the adult. The head may have well developed mouth parts and antennae; the thorax often bears three pairs of legs comparable to those of the adult; and the long abdomen may have additional legs for its support. The body of the larva may be smooth or hairy, white or brilliantly colored. Its chief aim in life is to eat as much as possible in as short a time as possible.

Larvae have various common names. Those of the moths and butterflies are called caterpillars. A *caterpillar* has a cylindrical body with well developed head, true legs on its thorax and five pairs of prolegs on its abdomen. A *maggot* is a legless cylindrical larva, which may or may not have a head; maggots are larval stages of flies, wasps, ants, and some beetles. A *grub* is a sluggish sort of larva with well developed head and thoracic legs but no abdominal legs; its body is usually curved. Grubs occur among the beetles. *Wireworms* are hard-shelled, short-legged larvae of certain beetles.

After a few months of active feeding, the larva goes into a resting stage, and is called a pupa. It may lie unprotected in the earth or on the ground, or it may be enveloped in a cocoon. Rare is the young naturalist who has not collected cocoons, and thrilled at the sight of the emerging moth. The transformation within the pupa results in a winged adult, but before it can fly certain final changes have to take place. As the insect emerges, its large clumsy abdomen trails behind and its wings hang limply. Clinging to a twig or stone, the adult may fan its wings to speed its circulation. As the blood moves into all parts of the body, the wings become rigid and the body organs expand to their proper proportions. Fluids in the thorax and abdomen of the pupa move into the

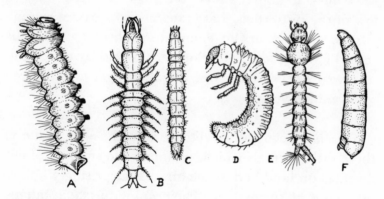

Larvae of insects have various names. Those of moths and butterflies (A) are caterpillars; those of Dobsonflies (B) are known as hellgrammites, of click beetles (C) are wireworms, of many other beetles (D) are grubs, of mosquitoes (E) are wigglers, and those of flies (F) are maggots.

wings and antennae. The chitinous rings of the skeleton become hardened, the flaccid wings become strong and firm. After a few hours the winged insect is ready to take off on its maiden flight, the reward for long months inside the pupal case.

In temperate regions, which include most of the United States, insects generally have but one generation, with one metamorphosis, a year. How to survive the unfavorable winter season is a problem solved in different ways among the various insect orders. Most of the grasshoppers and bugs overwinter as eggs; thus the beginning of metamorphosis is delayed until spring. In many other insects metamorphosis begins as soon as the eggs are laid. In the dragonflies and damselflies it is the nymph which lives through the winter by hibernating, and in many of the butterflies and moths, the larva survives the winter in hibernation. Adult insects which live through the winter are found among the bugs and beetles, and a few of the butterflies. Large insects, sometimes require two or three years to complete metamorphosis; the record for long larval development is held by the Seventeen-year Locust, where the larval changes take thirteen to seventeen years.

This has been but a glimpse into the way of life of those little animals which, although the smallest of our dwellers on land and in the air, are surprisingly able to take care of themselves. Their numerous adaptations, possible in the insect body plan, enable them to do many things which are impossible for other animals, to carry on many activities which are often spectacular. Their singleness of purpose, their strength and fortitude, their industry and uncanny instinctive knowledge of how to do things, gives us much to think about. The changes during metamorphosis provide the most dramatic spectacle to be found in nature. No wonder that insect study can become a lifelong hobby, often leading into a satisfying career.

Pyrgota fly attacks a June beetle in flight in order to lay her egg in its back

The walkingstick is a member of the grasshopper clan with such an elongated thorax and abdomen that the insect resembles an animated twig.

CHAPTER THREE

THE GRASSHOPPER CLAN

Grasshoppers and their relatives in the *Orthoptera* are large insects with chewing or biting mouth parts. Except for the flightless species of walking stick, they have two pairs of wings; the front pair is narrow and somewhat thickened, the hind pair membranous and used for flying. When not in use, the flight wings are folded like a fan against the body, beneath the protective front wings. In this order we find two of the most fascinating and grotesque of all insects: the praying mantis and the walkingstick. But among them also are some formidable insects which have been at times the scourge of mankind —locusts, Mormon crickets, and roaches.

An unusual feature of most of the species is their musical ability: the chirping of crickets, the call of the katydids, the drone of the grasshoppers. Singing is an accomplishment of the males, but both males and females have hearing organs to appreciate the music. In their life history, these insects go through a simple metamorphosis; in the juvenile stages they look like adults except for the smaller size and the absence of wings. Man's ally in keeping these insects in their place is the birds, which depend upon grasshoppers for about 10% of their diet. Locusts have been a staple food also for people in other lands, and for the American Indian in the West.

Short-horned Grasshoppers

These are the common grasshoppers of fields and meadows, with greenish or brownish bodies and hindwings which may be either transparent, or banded and colored. They get their name from the short antennae, which are less than half the body length. All feed upon plants, for which their scissor-like mouth parts are well adapted. Normally they are not destructive, but a large swarm, concentrating on crop plants and forage grasses, becomes a great menace. Their chief natural enemy is the sparrowhawk; but they are eaten by other hawks as well, and by owls, snakes, toads, and skunks.

Male grasshoppers sing in two different ways. The Lubber Grasshopper of the southern states and the Migratory Grasshopper rub the inner surface of the hind-leg against the lower edge of the forewing; the resulting sound is caused by the row of blunt spines on the hind-limb rasping against the forewing. This song is the familiar high-pitched buzz. Another method, used by the Carolina Grasshopper, consists of rubbing the edge of the hindwing against that of the forewing; these grasshoppers often sing while in flight. Hearing organs, found in both sexes, consist of an oval eardrum on each side of the first segment of the abdomen.

There are many kinds of grasshoppers. The CARO-LINA GRASSHOPPER has red hindwings with a black border. The MIGRATORY GRASSHOPPER and the DIFFERENTIAL GRASSHOPPER are two of the worst pests in the midwestern states. Most notorious is the ROCKY MOUNTAIN LOCUST which often invades the plains states and does great damage to crops.

The terms "grasshopper" and "locust" are often used in a confusing manner; actually a locust is a grasshopper. To make matters more confusing, some other insects, such as the cicadas, are also called locusts. The difference between a grasshopper and a locust depends more upon behavior than appearance. Individuals which stay at home, leading solitary lives and minding their own business, are known as grasshoppers. However when these same insects become crowded and the surrounding living conditions are favorable, they become nervous and have an overwhelming desire to travel. Then they become migratory grasshoppers or locusts. Elimination of their feeding grounds by drought, flood, or fire is one cause for the migratory movement. Also important are

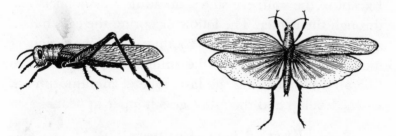

American Grasshopper (*left*) and Carolina Grasshopper (*right*) show the large hind legs and the narrow thickened forewings typical of the group.

such climatic factors as a warm dry winter. When the locusts' bodies become warmer than usual, they start to migrate spontaneously and in large numbers. Then swarms of locusts get on the move, eating everything in their path, until a change in the weather (rain, lower temperatures, storms) forces them to settle down.

Migrating locusts can cover surprising distances. African locusts have flown to England, and locust swarms have been seen 1200 miles at sea. Locust plagues still occur in the Mediterranean countries, as they have since biblical times. The most famous American locust plague took place in the 1870's, in the plains states just east of the Rockies. The skies of Nebraska were darkened by a locust swarm 100 miles wide and 300 miles long. Observers estimated there were 124 billion locusts in this flying army. These were Rocky Mountain Locusts, a species normally more restricted in its range.

In autumn female grasshoppers dig holes in the ground with the tip of the abdomen, and each lays a small package of twenty to a hundred eggs. The eggs remain alive but quiescent throughout the winter; they are the means by which grasshoppers survive from year to year. Except in the southern states, no adult grasshoppers live through the winter. The following spring the eggs hatch, and the resulting nymphs go through a succession of molts, after each of which the animal is larger and more like an adult. During the last stage of metamorphosis, wings develop and the adult grasshopper appears.

Long-horned Grasshoppers

Many people have heard katydids sing, but have not seen the delicately winged green insects responsible for the call. The slender antennae are much longer than the body, hence their "long-horned" title. These insects produce their "Katy-did, Katy-didn't" refrain by rubbing their wings together. The underside of the left forewing has a roughened edge which is rubbed over a ridge on the upperside of the right forewing. Like other grasshoppers, only the males are vocal. Both males and females hear with eardrums located on the front legs.

The BUSH KATYDID lives in tall weeds and grasses during the day; other species live in the trees. Although green is their normal color, pink individuals are sometimes found. The female deposits flattened, oval eggs on the surface or along the margin of leaves. Like the short-horned grasshoppers, katydids die in autumn but their eggs survive. The following spring the eggs hatch and go through seven nymphal stages before becoming full-grown, winged adults.

A close relative of the katydid is the MORMON CRICKET, a clumsy grasshopper-like insect with wings

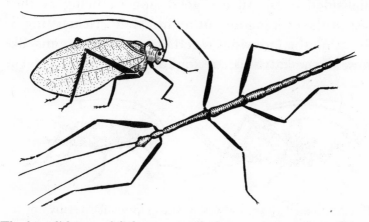

The katydid (*upper left*) has unusually long antennae; the walking-stick is one of the few wingless insects.

far too short for flying. The hind margin of the first segment of the thorax projects like a shield over the forward part of the abdomen. This is a western species, living normally in small numbers in the foothills and the mountains. Under conditions favorable for raising large families, the Mormon Cricket becomes a serious pest, threatening complete crop failure. Millions of the crawling, hopping insects swarm over corn fields and vegetable gardens. To trap them, special metal guards and fences are erected which collect yard-high piles of the writhing animals. The early Mormons waged a continual battle against them. One year when they were especially numerous, the Mormon crops were saved by flocks of sea gulls which devoured the crickets. A monument to the sea gulls was erected by the grateful Mormons in Temple Square, Salt Lake City.

FIELD CRICKETS and HOUSE CRICKETS are flattened insects with long thread-like antennae; some have wedge-shaped bodies, others cylindrical and parallel-sided ones. All are good singers, being at their best in the evening and at night. Male crickets sing by vibrating the forewings together; auditory organs, like those of the katydids, are found on the front legs. The

The Mormon Cricket (*left*) is a grasshopper-like relative of the katydid; the common Field Cricket (*right*) is the vocal member of the true cricket clan.

common Field Cricket is black; it often wanders into homes, doing little damage. The House Cricket is a straw-colored European species, made famous by Dickens in his tale of "The Cricket on the Hearth." These crickets can be kept as pets in cages and fed lettuce and moist bread. The tempo of the chirping depends upon the temperature so closely that one can often tell the air temperature by counting the number of chirps per minute, dividing the result by 4 and adding 40. Thus if you count 100 chirps per minute, the temperature will be about 65 degrees. Cricket eggs are laid singly in the ground; like the grasshoppers they develop through a succession of wingless stages by simple metamorphosis. Crickets are plant feeders, and as a result sometimes injure crops by cutting seedlings and eating grains from fruiting heads of cereals. On the other hand the tree crickets aid man by eating aphids and scale insects.

Other Orthoptera

WALKINGSTICK. This slender, elongated insect shows a remarkable degree of protective adaptation in its resemblance to the twig on which it is resting. The unusually long thorax may be half the entire body length. The common northern species is wingless, but a Florida walkingstick is winged. Walkingsticks reach their greatest development in the tropics. In spite of their camouflage, sharp-eyed birds, such as grackles, feed on them, as do lizards, rodents, and the carnivorous mantids. Young walkingsticks are greenish, but as they grow older they become brown. Walkingsticks spend much of their time among the foliage of trees, where they feed on the leaves. Slow in movement, their chief defense is a foul-smelling substance secreted by glands in the thorax. Ordinarily these insects are not destructive; but when they sometimes occur in great numbers, they may strip the leaves from an entire tree. Walkingsticks survive the winter as eggs which develop in spring through five or six nymphal stages. At times, when a tree is populated by a great number of females, the eggs, dropping singly to the ground, sound like the patter of raindrops. The eggs remain buried in the fallen leaves all winter.

MANTIDS. These are the fearless hunters of the insect world, armed with powerful forelegs which have given up the function of walking to specialize in grasping prey. The other four legs are of equal size and are used in walking and climbing. The triangular head bears long antennae and very large compound eyes. Mantids are unusual in being able to turn their head around and look over their shoulder. Their gray or brownish green color is a protection as they hide among the leaves, waiting with forelegs uplifted as in prayer but actually ready to pounce on any unwary insect. In spite of this fearsome appearance, the mantid is harmless and will neither bite nor sting when handled. Mantids eat each other as well as insects in general; for this reason it is impossible to keep more than one mantid alive in a cage at the same time. Female mantids lay several hundred eggs in a parchment-like braided egg case which surrounds a twig; these are common objects on shrubs in autumn and winter. In spring the small mantids go through the succession of molting stages which eventually results in the adult winged insect. Young mantids are light in color, darkening as they mature.

The Carolina Mantis is a native species found in the

southern states; it is one of the smaller mantids, about two inches in length. Also about two inches long is the European Mantis introduced into upstate New York about fifty years ago. Another immigrant is the Chinese Mantis, a large insect three or four inches in length, which came from Asia to Pennsylvania in 1896. Both species were accidentally introduced but are now purposely cultivated to keep in check injurious insects.

ROACHES. Cockroaches, in spite of their ill repute, are interesting members of the grasshopper clan. They are sturdy, good-sized insects which have unfortunately become persistent and unwelcome guests in houses and barns. Some species infest restaurants and food-storage buildings, others invade bathrooms and kitchens. They leave a disagreeable odor, contaminate food, and chew holes in clothing; but it has not been proved that they carry diseases.

The first segment of the thorax in a roach is so overdeveloped that it completely hides the head. The slender

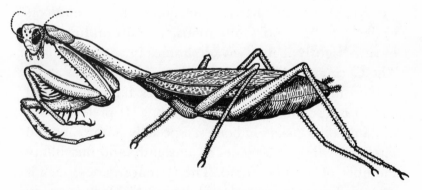

The Carolina Mantis is a fearsome-looking animal with powerful forelegs suited for catching its insect prey; it is harmless to man, however, neither biting nor stinging.

antennae are longer than the body and very conspicuous. Long agile legs enable roaches to run quickly, and make them difficult to catch. The winged individuals have two pairs of wings; the front pair is leathery and brown or yellow, usually held folded along the back. Many females have short useless wings. It comes as a surprise to discover that they are actually very clean animals, spending as much time on their personal appearance as do cats. They clean their body with their spiny legs, and groom their antennae and legs in their mouths. Roaches usually avoid the light, hiding by day and foraging at night. Females lay their eggs in dark corners, gluing them to walls and similar surfaces.

All our roaches are thought to be immigrants. Largest is the American Cockroach, a reddish brown insect about an inch and a half in length, with well developed wings. This is believed to have immigrated to the United States in slave ships, and to have found outdoor living in the southern states much to its liking. Farther north it comes into homes during cold weather. The American Cockroach usually has its permanent home outdoors under porches and foundations, in outbuildings and barns. Nightly it may invade homes in search of food. The German Cockroach is a lighter-brown insect about half an inch in length, with two black bars on its head end; it is also known as the Crotonbug. It prefers to live in damp dark places in houses, especially bathrooms and kitchens, where it becomes an unsightly and unsanitary member of the household. The Oriental Cockroach is intermediate in size, and dark brown to black in color; it has the habits of the American cockroach. In this species we find an interesting difference in the appearance of males and females, the latter being practically wingless, with wide plump abdomen.

Among the grasshopper clan are many more members with special characteristics. The mole crickets have spade-like front legs which enable them to burrow underground. The thorax of the pygmy or grouse locusts has a long backward extension as a protection for the abdomen; these locusts have the rare ability to survive the winter as adults. The sand crickets of the Pacific coast live under stones and in loose soil; their eastern relatives create a snug home for themselves by rolling up a leaf and tying it with silk. These are but a representative few of the many species of Orthoptera found in the United States; they are typical however of the main groups in this order.

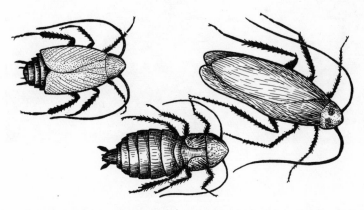

In the Oriental Cockroach the male (*upper left*) has longer wings and smaller abdomen than the female (*center*); the American Cockroach (*right*) is larger than either of these.

The cicada is a broad-headed and clumsy bug which emerges from a nymph case (*upper left*) which remains as a replica of its former owner.

CHAPTER FOUR

THE SUCKING INSECTS: BUGS

The term "bug" in popular usage means any small insect. To an entomologist however a bug is a special kind of insect with features which set it apart from all other insects. These true bugs, which belong to the order *Hemiptera,* can be recognized by their wings. The front pair, which is larger than the hind pair, has the basal part of the wing thickened and leathery. The hind wings are thin and membranous. Bugs are also characterized by sucking mouth parts; these sharply pointed mandibles and maxillae are sheathed in a slender segmented beak arising from the front of the head. Included in our insect parade are such plant-feeders as the stink bugs, squash bugs, chinch bugs, lace bugs, and plant bugs; such carnivorous types as the ambush bugs and assassin bugs; and such water-dwellers as the water boatmen, back swimmers, water scorpions, giant water bugs, and water striders.

Closely related to these bugs are insects which have normal wings, the front wings not having a thickened basal portion, and whose beak arises on the base rather than the front of the head. These are mostly plant-feeders, some of them very harmful to crops. Our insect parade has, as representatives of these insects, the various "hoppers," cicadas, aphids, and scale insects.

Plant-feeding Bugs

STINK BUGS. These bugs have a broad, shield-shaped body when viewed from above, and possess scent glands on the thorax which can emit foul odors. Stink bugs vary from half an inch to three-quarters of an inch in length. Various species are either green, brown, or vari-colored. Stink bug eggs are like little ornamented barrels; they are glued side by side on the surface of leaves. A common stink bug is the gaily colored Harlequin Bug, whose body and wings are shiny blue-black, marked with red. It came to this country from Mexico, finding life on cabbages and other plants of the mustard

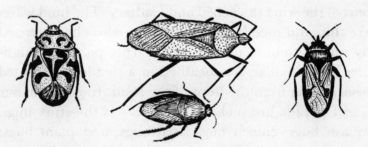

The Harlequin Bug (*left*) is gaily colored black and red; the common Squash Bug (*upper center*) is a speckled brown; the burrowing Ground Bug (*lower center*) is brownish black; and the Chinch Bug (*right*) is conspicuously marked with white, black, or red.

– 60 –

family much to its liking. One of the few commendable traits of the English sparrow is its fondness for Harlequin Bugs. The Ground Bug is another kind of stink bug; it is a green or brownish black insect whose burrowing habit is made possible by legs adapted for digging. The Southern Green Stink Bug lives on tomato plants and other vegetables; unlike the previous two species, it is limited to the southeastern states.

SQUASH BUGS. These small bugs have the membranous portion of the forewing marked by conspicuous parallel veins. The offensive odor of squash bugs is especially noticeable at close range. The common Squash Bug has speckled brown thorax and forewings. Adults live through the winter hiding beneath piles of leaves and rubbish. Squash bug eggs are laid on plants and, like those of other bugs, pass through a succession of nymphal stages before becoming winged adults. Squash bugs, frequently found on squash and pumpkin plants, cause leaves to wilt, and plants to die. The Box Elder Bug, which is red and black, feeds on maple foliage; in the Midwest this bug finds winter quarters inside houses.

CHINCH BUGS are smaller than stink or squash bugs, being about half an inch in length; many are conspicuously marked with white, black, or red. The Chinch Bug is a pest on wheat, corn, rye, and barley throughout most of the United States. Its sap-sucking habits cause wilting and death of crops. Chinch bugs spend the winter as adults, hibernating beneath clumps of grass and rubbish. The eggs are laid in early spring on roots or lower stems of grasses and cereal crops. One generation of adults appears in early summer, another in early fall. Although this bug has wings it rarely uses them, preferring to go on foot from field to field. It has been estimated that the Chinch Bug has cost the wheat and corn growers of our country about half a billion dollars!

LACE BUGS are tiny whitish insects, a fraction of an inch in length. They live on the underside of leaves of woody plants. They are aptly named, for the delicate sculpturing of the flattened wings and thorax gives one the impression of fine lace. Lace bug eggs are protected in brown cones, attached to leaves; they hatch into spiny nymphs. Adults can survive winter beneath leaves and piles of woodland debris. It is the Sycamore Lace Bug which causes the browning of sycamore leaves in late summer.

The largest family is that of the PLANT BUGS, small insects which can be identified by a triangular area in the margin of the forewing. Most plant bugs are a quarter of an inch or less in length. Like many other bugs, they can live through the winter as adults. They are quite harmful to cultivated plants, for they inject a toxic substance while feeding, which deforms or kills the host plant; they cause stunting of alfalfa and grasses. Common on apple, peach, and pear trees throughout eastern and central United States is the Tarnished Plant Bug, a yellowish brown species with yellow head and three narrow

The Sycamore Lace Bug (*left*) is a tiny but exquisitely sculptured insect; the Four-lined Plant Bug (*center*) is green with a red head; the Tarnished Plant Bug (*right*) varies from brown to black.

reddish stripes. The Four-lined Leaf Bug is a colorful green insect with orange-red head and four black stripes on the thorax and front wings. This bug causes browning and curling of leaves on currant bushes.

Insect-eating Bugs

AMBUSH BUGS are stout-bodied insects whose small size (about a quarter of an inch) gives no indication of their fearlessness in catching and eating their plant-feeding cousins. Their yellowish green color is excellent camouflage as they lie in wait on flowers, especially those of goldenrod, for their unsuspecting prey. Although slow-moving, they have powerful grasping forelegs and deadly beaks. Ambush bugs can capture insects many times their size, feeding on such large species as butterflies and bees. Piercing mouth parts, used in the plant-feeding bugs to suck sap from plants, are employed by the ambush bugs to drain blood from the bodies of their victims.

ASSASSIN BUGS are another group of insect eaters. They are somber brown and black bugs, growing to a length of an inch and a half. Although they do not have specially modified grasping legs like the ambush bugs, they still are adept at catching their prey. Some species

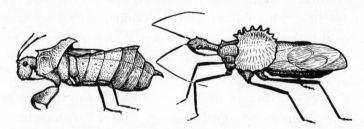

The Ambush Bug (*left*) and Giant Wheel Bug (*right*) are two of the carnivorous bugs.

are wingless, or have short useless wings. One of the assassin bugs is known as the Giant Wheel Bug because of its semicircular crest, edged with teeth and thus resembling a cogwheel. Wheel Bugs are most common in the southern states; they are bronze-gray in color, with powerful biting mouth parts and so should be handled carefully. Wheel Bugs are helpful allies of man in reducing the numbers of caterpillars and injurious adult insects. Another species, known as the Kissing Bug, enters houses in search of prey. Sticky hairs on the head and body often collect lint and dust as this bug pokes into corners and crevices looking for other insects; for this reason it is also known as the Masked Hunter. It searches chiefly for bedbugs, but it occasionally inflicts painful bites upon human victims.

Water-dwelling Bugs

Many kinds of bugs have taken to the water. These have become adept at walking on the water, swimming, or crawling beneath its surface. They have also adapted their breathing to suit such a way of life. As a result the water bugs have some extremely interesting habits.

WATER STRIDERS. As we watch these agile, long-legged insects skate over the surface of the water, we cannot help but marvel at their ability to do what is impossible for other animals. When Water Striders jump on the water, they only dent its surface with a dimple-like impression. A covering of fine water-repellent hairs on the legs traps air and is responsible for the water strider's unique accomplishment. Water striders have narrow bodies and extremely long slender legs. The front pair is modified for grasping food, the two other pairs are stilt-like supports for the body. In action they skate over the water by pushing with the middle pair of legs and steering with the hind pair; the forelegs are held aloft, ready to catch a meal. These insects have wings, but they are short and rarely used; when disturbed they will skate away on the water's surface rather than attempt flight. Water Striders spend most of their

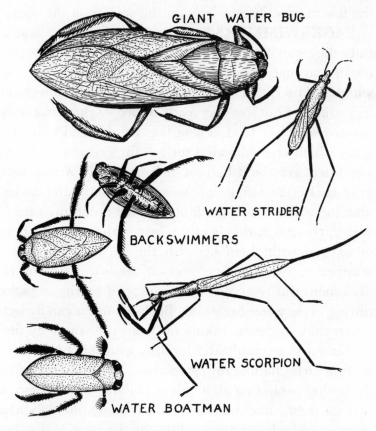

GIANT WATER BUG

WATER STRIDER

BACKSWIMMERS

WATER SCORPION

WATER BOATMAN

Many bugs have made themselves at home on or in the water; they are able to swim and dive as well as to walk on the surface of the water or crawl along the bottom.

lives on the top of the water, sometimes congregating in large numbers in quiet coves; they feed on insects, dead or alive, which happen to fall into the water. During winter, and at other times when their aquatic homes dry up, they hide under stones and logs. The females deposit their eggs in the tissues of water plants, or on any floating object; the larvae live in the water until they reach the adult stage. A salt-water species, one of the few marine insects, lives on the surface of the ocean.

BACKSWIMMERS have bodies lighter than water, thus they can float on its surface. They lead this lazy life in a strange fashion; floating on their backs, they use wings and body as a boat, with head down and long hind legs stretched out like oars ready to propel them instantly toward safety or food. These legs are fringed with stiff hairs which give increased surface for swimming. Back-swimmers are about half an inch in length, with pearly gray backs (their underside when swimming) and darker abdomens. As a special adaptation for breathing underwater, these skin-divers of the bug clan carry a supply of oxygen with them beneath the surface. The air is trapped in two hairy grooves on the lower side of the abdomen; this reservoir of air is tapped by the spiracles during underwater breathing. Backswimmers can fly well when they so desire, taking off from the water by first turning a somersault and landing on their belly, then getting airborne like tiny seaplanes. At night they often fly in droves circling about electric lights which seem to attract them. Backswimmers eat insects, but they also prey on tadpoles and small fish, for the later reason becoming a nuisance in fish-rearing ponds. However this damage is offset by their being, in turn, food for larger fish. Backswimmers may bite when handled, with the effect of a bee sting. The females insert their eggs in plant tissues or leave them glued to plant stems; nymphs and adults both may hibernate at the bottom of ponds, or remain active all winter.

WATER BOATMEN. The bodies of these bugs are heavier than water, so they usually rest on the bottom or crawl among aquatic plants. They are flatter than Backswimmers, with wider heads and an oval shape, and swim in the more usual fashion—right side up. Water Boatmen are less courageous hunters, content with browsing on algae and other underwater vegetation, and on the minute aquatic animals found among these plants. The adults are winged and, like Backswimmers, are often attracted to lights. The oar-like hindlegs are an aid in swimming. When going underwater they carry a bubble of air with them as an auxiliary air supply, held among the hairs on the underside of the body or under the wings. From this the spiracles get air when the bug is underwater. Unlike Backswimmers, Water Boatmen do not bite when caught. The eggs are attached to aquatic plants by short stalks; they hatch into nymphs which live underwater, breathing directly through their body walls. These insects, and their eggs, are collected and ground up in the preparation of commercial fish food.

WATER SCORPIONS get their name from the scorpion-like grasping forelegs and the long breathing tube at the tip of the abdomen which looks like a scorpion's tail. This breathing tube is a modification of the appendages known as cerci; it is a snorkel which functions as well as the human invention in carrying air to the bug while it is moving beneath the surface. The elongated body bears long, slender legs on which the Water Scorpion crawls along the muddy bottom of ponds. They swim awkwardly and rarely fly, even though they have wings. Water Scorpions can bite but they do not "sting" with their breathing tube. Their diet consists of eggs and insects in other stages of development which chance to be in the water; it also includes fish eggs and even small fish.

GIANT WATER BUGS are the largest of the true bugs; American species reach a length of several inches while tropical relatives grow to be four inches long. They are the common large, brown, oval and flattened bugs found in ponds and quiet streams. The forelegs are powerful in grasping prey; the hindlegs are modified for swimming. These large water bugs can inflict a bite made more painful because of the injection of a digestive fluid. Giant water bugs lurk on muddy bottoms, partly hidden, until they see a possible meal; then darting out, they usually are successful in capturing their prey. They eat other aquatic insects, snails, tadpoles, and small fish. These bugs also are a menace in fish-rearing ponds. At night they take to the air and collect around lights in noisy swarms. In fact one species is found there so frequently it is known as the Electric Light Bug.

Treehoppers and Their Kin

TREEHOPPERS are readily recognized by the peculiar shape of the thorax, which extends over the head and abdomen and gives the insect a humpbacked appearance. Some treehoppers look very much like brown thorns as they perch on a twig. As their name suggests they hop rather than fly. They are small insects, causing most of their damage to plants not by sucking the sap but by the habit of slitting open the bark of twigs in order to deposit the eggs in the plant tissues. This causes the terminal part of the twig to die. Treehoppers overwinter as eggs; in spring these hatch into nymphs which drop to the ground and complete their metamorphosis while feeding on grasses and weeds. As adults, they then return to the trees to feed and lay their eggs. Two common species are the Buffalo Treehopper found on orchard trees, and the Hickory Treehopper.

PLANTHOPPERS are likewise small insects which feed on plant sap; they differ from treehoppers in having the antennae arise below and behind the eyes. Like treehoppers they jump rather than use their wings in flight. In some species the head is snout-like or prolonged into a horn. Other species look like small moths. Planthopper nymphs are usually covered with a powdery white coating of wax.

More colorful and also of greater economic importance are the LEAFHOPPERS—slender insects with small hairlike antennae arising between the eyes, and with a double row of spines on the hindlegs. They too

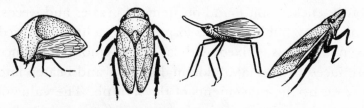

Strange and grotesque body forms are found among the 'hoppers: Buffalo Treehopper (*left*), Froghopper or Spittlebug (*second from left*), Scolops or Planthopper, and Red-banded Leafhopper (*right*).

– 69 –

are small insects, about half an inch in length, which feed by sucking plant sap. Planthoppers and treehoppers give off small quantities of honeydew, but some leafhoppers do so with such force that they squirt out the sweet liquid as drops; for this reason they are also called Sharpshooters. The Red-banded Leafhopper of eastern United States feeds on garden flowers and vegetables; it is a conspicuous insect with bright green stripes on its red wings. The Blue Dodger, one of the sharpshooter varieties, can be found on sunflowers. A common species on vegetables is the Potato Leafhopper. Leafhoppers cause discoloration and wilting of foliage by sucking the sap and plugging up the water-conducting channels of stems; they also carry virus diseases from plant to plant. Leafhoppers spend the winter as eggs, hidden in plant tissues, or as nymphs and adults buried among dead leaves.

SPITTLEBUGS, or FROGHOPPERS, are small brown or gray insects, rarely over half an inch in length and sometimes as broad as long. Because of their squat shape they resemble little frogs; like all other "hoppers" they jump rather than fly when disturbed. These insects are interesting because the nymphs surround themselves with a frothy mass of "spittle"; this is the familiar frog-spit or cuckoo-spit found on stems of grasses and weeds. This foamy bubble-bath is formed from a liquid emitted from the anus, mixed with a mucilaginous substance produced by special abdominal glands, and beaten into a froth by the movements of the nymph. The value of the spittle to the insect is not known for a certainty, but it undoubtedly keeps the nymphs from drying out or being overheated in the summer sun. One or several of the tiny nymphs can be found in the center of the frothy mass, where they live until after the last molt. Then they leave their unusual home for a short carefree life on the foliage of plants.

Cicadas

CICADAS. These musical insects are also known as Harvest Flies and as Locusts; some seventy-five different kinds live in the United States. Cicadas are large robust insects, growing to a length of two inches, with protruding eyes and cellophane-like wings with coarse veins. The forewings are much larger than the hindwings. Their claim to fame in the insect parade lies in their special musical instrument, and in their unusual life cycle. The Dog-day Cicada is a common species; it has a black body with green markings. The nymph lives underground for two to five years, then appears in July or August to produce the sounds associated with sultry late-summer days. The Periodical Cicada or Seventeen-year Locust lives underground for a much longer period of time before becoming a red-eyed and red-veined adult which suddenly appears in trees in May or June. Cicadas insert their eggs in slits in the branches of trees; it is this egg-laying habit which does most damage, killing the terminal portion of the twigs.

A cicada's musical instrument consists of two cavities hidden beneath plates in the part of the thorax next to the abdomen. Each cavity has a yellowish membrane at one end, a mirror-like membrane at the other. On one side is an oval ribbed structure, the tymbal, with which the cicada makes its penetrating sounds. The tymbal is set in vibration by special muscles; the other parts of the music box control the volume and quality of the song. Thus the high-pitched whirr or drone of a cicada is actually a kind of drumming. Each species has its own characteristic music by which a trained listener can identify it. Certainly no insect can compete with the cicada in strength and volume of its singing.

When cicada eggs hatch they fall to the ground and the young nymph burrows into the soil, beginning a long life in darkness and feeding on roots. Few animals spend so much of their lives in youthful preparation for a relatively short adult existence. The Seventeen-year Locust (it is a thirteen-year locust in the South) spends seventeen long years in going through the stages of metamorphosis underground. With unfailing accuracy, it knows when the seventeen years are over and begins tunneling to the surface, aided by specially enlarged front feet. If the soil is moist, the nymph may make a protective chimney around the exit of its burrow. The emerging nymph crawls up on a tree, basks in the sun for a time until the larval skin splits along the back; the winged adult crawls out of the slit, leaving the gray skin as a vestige of its long nymphal existence. The predict-

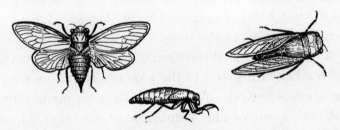

The Seventeen-year Locust (*left*, nymph at center) takes that length of time to complete its development; the common Dog-day Cicada matures in two to five years (*right*).

able and sudden appearance of the adult cicadas gets considerable publicity as the swarms cover the branches and leaves of trees. These hordes provide unexpected feasts for sparrows and grackles.

Each different brood of cicadas has its own seventeen-year cycle. Therefore the appearance of these insects is not just at seventeen-year intervals. One large brood which appeared in 1928 reappeared in 1945 and will return in 1962. Another brood, in a different part of the country, appeared in 1933 returned in 1950 and will again mature in 1967. Various sections of the country have their own broods. When these appear, the great numbers of females laying their eggs in the branches and twigs of trees do great harm in stunting and deforming the trees, although they seldom kill the entire tree. In spite of the damage they do, we cannot help being fascinated by the predictable time cycle of the return of the cicadas.

Aphids and Scale Insects

APHIDS, also known as Plant Lice, are at the same time the most injurious and the most interesting of insects. Adult aphids have pear-shaped bodies whose forewings are larger than the hindwings. In some species a pair of small tubes known as cornicles project rearward from the abdomen; these secrete a waxy material which covers the aphid body with a mass of white waxy fibers. The feeding habits of aphids not only cause severe damage to many crop plants, but also are a means of carrying virus plant diseases. An American aphid—the Grape Phylloxera—which reached France almost wiped out the French wine industry. Other species cause plant galls; perhaps you have seen these cone-shaped or spiny growths on leaves and not realized they were caused by insects. Common aphid galls are the cockscomb gall on elm leaves and the spiny gall of witch hazel.

While feeding on plant sap, aphids excrete the surplus water, mixed with sugars. This honeydew, already mentioned as an excretion of other bugs, in the aphids gives rise to one of the most remarkable relationships between two kinds of animals. One species of ant carefully collects the eggs of the Corn-root Aphid and takes care of them during the winter, protecting them in the ant colony as carefully as a farmer does his cattle. When the eggs hatch the ants transport the young aphids to "pastures" which the ants have uncovered among the roots of weeds. Later, when the corn fields are planted, the ants again transfer their aphids, this time to the corn roots. While taking care of them, the ants feast on the honeydew provided by the aphids. Corn-root Aphids have often been called the "cows" of ants; they certainly reveal a remarkable example of cooperative living.

Aphids have a complex life history which involves a succession of female generations which rear families without fathers, and give birth to living young. The cycle begins with oval black eggs, placed in crevices of bark and similar places by the female, which live through the winter. With the coming of spring they hatch into wingless females which mature in a short time to give birth to another generation of wingless females. Late in spring a generation of winged females develops which migrates to another host plant, where the cycle of wingless female generations is repeated. By the end of summer a generation of winged males and females appear; these mate, after which the females lay the eggs which survive the winter. With such a reproductive potential, aphids would increase in overwhelming numbers were it not for the appetite of our songbirds—especially warblers, chickadees, and vireos. Aphids are also kept in check by parasitic wasps and ladybird beetles.

SCALE INSECTS are another harmful but fascinating group. They have attained such a highly specialized parasitic life that they have given up many of the characteristic structures and activities of ordinary insects, some species being as sedentary as barnacles or sea anemones. Scale insects are so small they are likely to be overlooked, except when they congregate in colonies. Some are called soft scales, and are covered with a waxy coat. In this group are the mealybugs, oval segmented insects which crawl about on plants, their bodies coated with white wax. Only the males have wings, but they die shortly after mating and as a result are rarely seen. The Citrus Mealybug thrives on all kinds of plants indoors, and outdoors on citrus trees in Florida and California.

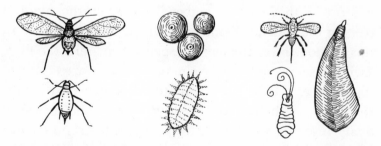

Strange parasites are found among the aphids (*left*), scale insects (San Jose Scale, *upper center*, Citrus Mealybug, *lower center,* and Oyster-shell Scale, *right*). The winged male and wingless female Oyster-shell Scale are also shown.

Others are called armored scales, because they cover themselves with a hard scale made from wax which is secreted by their bodies; under this they pass their lives, like a limpet beneath its shell. Some scales are circular, some shaped like oyster shells. These are often stuck to the bark of trees and seem wholly unlike living insects. Under the scale each adult female—eyeless, wingless, and legless—settles down for life, fastening her mouth permanently to the host plant. The males possess wings, but cannot eat since they have no mouths. Scale insects travel from one plant to another as nymphs, when they are known as crawlers. At this stage the scale insect has legs and antennae, but after the first molt these structures are lost. The San Jose Scale, which first appeared in California in 1880, is an armored scale now widespread on many kinds of fruit and ornamental trees. The Oyster-shell Scale lives on the bark of apple and pear trees, and in some regions on various deciduous and evergreen trees.

Some of the scale insects have been found useful by man. The larvae of the Lac Insect of the East Indies exude a reddish resinous material in such quantities that it forms a thick honeycombed layer over the twigs of trees in the Banyan Family, on which the scale feeds. In this resinous layer the females spend their immotile lives. Twigs, insects, and their resinous secretion are collected together, and from them a material is secured which is the basis of shellac and sealing wax. The Cochineal Scale Insect is a native of Mexico and feeds on cactus; it produces cochineal, a scarlet or orange dye. With the development of aniline dyes by the chemist, cochineal dye has become less important. The Tamarisk Scale of the arid Mediterranean regions produces a honeydew which solidifies in sugary layers on the leaves. This is thought to be the manna mentioned in the Bible.

This is but an introduction to the many colorful and interesting insects to be found among the bugs and their allies. The variety of their activities and the ingenuity of their adaptations in feeding habits and locomotion should give us more respect for the term "bug" next time we hear it used. Those of us who raise plants either for pleasure or profit will find it worth while to be able to recognize the harmful bugs from the harmless ones. When the battle begins every spring, as we plant our seeds hopefully, a knowledge of these injurious bugs and how to control them will help us win the struggle against them and their destructive habits.

Head-on view of a Treehopper

The Japanese Beetle is a colorful but destructive member of the beetle clan.

CHAPTER FIVE

THE CHEWING
INSECTS: BEETLES

Beetles, like bugs, are relatively small insects; many are
less than an inch in length and only a few grow to two
or three inches. Under the more favorable living conditions of the tropics, beetle species become larger, some
being insect "giants" five inches in length. The leathery
or hard pair of forewings, which form a protective cover
for the underlying pair of flight wings, is often shiny and
colorful. Beetles have been called "nature's gems"
because of their many brilliant hues; they could also
be called the "knights in shining armor" of the insect
world.

The mouth parts of beetles are remarkably efficient
tools for getting food. They are of the chewing type, with
well developed mandibles strong enough to crush seeds,
gnaw through wood, or pinch one's finger in a firm grip.
In some kinds of beetles the mandibles are slender and

grooved; through them the beetle can suck the blood of its prey. The weevil's mouth parts are at the end of an elongated snout. Among the beetles in our insect parade we find many plant-feeders: click beetles, long-horned beetles, wood-boring beetles, bark beetles, leaf beetles, scarab beetles, stag beetles, and snout beetles. Those that feed on insects and other small animals are the tiger beetles, ground beetles, rove beetles, lady beetles, and fireflies. Beetles, like bugs, have in their group some water-dwelling species. These are found among the water scavenger beetles, diving beetles and whirligig beetles. Useful in disposing of the remains of dead animals are the carrion beetles.

Beetles go through a complete metamorphosis. The eggs hatch into larvae which live either under or above ground; some, like the wireworm and woodborer, are in this stage more destructive than at any other time in the beetle's life history. After a period of gluttonous eating, the larva becomes a pupa which in turn hatches into the winged adult. Most species have but one generation a year. Beetles only rarely overwinter as eggs; usually it is as larvae or pupae that they survive cold weather.

Plant-feeding Beetles

CLICK BEETLES. These dull-colored brown or gray beetles have flattened bodies and short legs; they grow to a length of half an inch. If put on their back, they can flip over to the accompaniment of the clicking sound which gives them their name. Click beetles can turn over because of a projection of the first segment of the thorax which fits into a socket on the underside of the second segment. By arching the back, this projection snaps into its socket and the beetle turns over onto its underside. The adults are vegetarians but do little damage. The eggs, laid in the soil among the roots of grasses, hatch into larvae known as wireworms which are very destructive to field crops and garden vegetables. The Wheat Wireworm, larva of a common click beetle, feeds on the roots and shoots of germinating wheat.

LONG-HORNED BEETLES have very long antennae and elongated bodies; they also have well developed mandibles, with which adults can girdle twigs and branches. In some species the body and forewings are covered with scales or hair. Long-horned beetles are sluggish insects; although they have wings, they rarely fly. The eggs, laid in crevices in bark, hatch into destructive larvae known as woodborers which can be

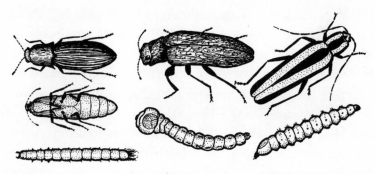

Click Beetles (*left*, upper and lower surface and wireworm larva) are dull-colored brown or gray beetles; Metallic Woodborers (*center*, with larva) are blue, green or bronze beetles; Longhorned Beetles (*right*, with larva) have well-developed mandibles used in girdling trees.

– 81 –

found in living or dead trees, just beneath the bark. The life cycle of these beetles is unusually long, requiring in some species four years to grow from egg to adult. Winter is spent in the larva stage. During its lifetime the woodboring larva ruins and blemishes standing timber, and eats through furniture and flooring. The larvae can often be heard in woodpiles as they gnaw their way through the wood; they also leave little telltale piles of sawdust. The Round-headed Apple Tree Borer, common east of the Rocky Mountains, bores into the base of the tree, often killing the tree by girdling it.

The METALLIC WOODBORERS are hard-bodied beetles about an inch in length, flat or cylindrical in shape and often colored bright metallic blues, greens, and bronze. The forewings have a corrugated surface. The insect seems headless when viewed from above because the head is beneath the first segment of the thorax. Adults are relatively harmless, spending their time in the woods getting nectar from flowers or just sunning themselves on a tree trunk, occasionally eating some foliage. The eggs, laid in the bark, hatch into white or yellowish larvae known as tree borers. These lead a more destructive life, feeding on wood, and spending the winter in the live sapwood, where they leave sawdust-filled tunnels just under the bark. The Flat-headed Apple Tree Borer however attacks healthy trees; other species live in trees already rotted or dead.

POWDER-POST BEETLES, widespread throughout the eastern states, are much more harmful insects whose white larvae bore into floor timbers, posts, and similar wooden structures leaving them honeycombed with tunnels. The sawdust is sometimes pushed out to the surface through tiny holes and left in small cone-shaped piles. Adult Powder-Post Beetles are reddish brown with elongated bodies a quarter of an inch in length.

BARK BEETLES, also known as ENGRAVER BEETLES, are some of our smallest beetles, about an eighth of an inch in length with cylindrical brown or black bodies. They live beneath the bark of trees, cutting tunnels on the surface of the wood. These beetles create characteristic patterns, often of an artistic design, by their tunneling habits. Adults gnaw a main corridor with notches along the sides in each of which an egg is laid. As the larvae develop they extend these lateral galleries, until at the end of their tunnels they have become pupae. When ready to emerge, they cut exit holes through

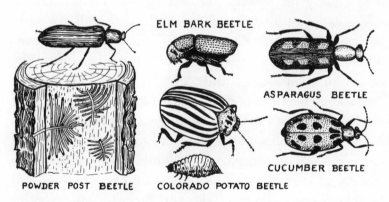

ELM BARK BEETLE

ASPARAGUS BEETLE

CUCUMBER BEETLE

POWDER POST BEETLE   COLORADO POTATO BEETLE

Powder-Post Beetles bore into wooden structures; related Engraver Beetles leave galleries in timber. The European Elm Bark Beetle carries the spores of the Dutch Elm disease. Other injurious beetles are found among the Leaf Beetles: Asparagus, Cucumber and Colorado Potato Beetles.

the bark. Some species attack living trees and damage them by girdling. Interesting bark beetles, known as Ambrosia or Timber Beetles, cultivate fungus gardens in their galleries; they do not eat the wood, but depend upon the fungus for food. In many species the adults keep the burrows filled with fresh fungi, and take time to feed it to the larvae. They also houseclean carefully, removing the excreted material left by the larvae. When a female flies to a new tree to start her own galleries, she carries with her some spores of the fungus which are the source of the new gardens. The European Bark Beetle carries the spores of the Dutch elm disease, a serious threat to many New England towns with their elm-lined streets.

LEAF BEETLES are small, usually oval, brightly colored beetles less than half an inch in length. Adults feed chiefly on flowers and leaves; the larvae have a wider range of food preference and as a result are more destructive, often feeding on roots and boring into stems. These beetles survive winter as adults, hibernating beneath piles of leaves and rubbish. The head of the Asparagus Beetle tapers to a narrow neck before joining the thorax; it is a colorful beetle, with blue-green wings marked with yellow, and a red thorax. As its name indicates, it feeds on asparagus. Cucumber Beetles feed on a variety of vegetables including cucumbers, melons, and beans; they eat both foliage and flowers. Most species are yellow with dark spots or stripes. A colorful but notorious leaf beetle is the Colorado Potato Beetle, whose yellow body with black stripes is far too well known to every gardener. It was originally a harmless species of the Colorado region feeding on wild members of the Nightshade Family. When the potato was introduced into the United States, the beetle transferred its activities to this new and far more plentiful member of the Nightshade Family. Now the beetle is a pest throughout this country, and has even invaded Europe.

SCARAB BEETLES. This large family of beetles has several features by which it can easily be recognized. Adults are one to three inches in length, and include the largest beetles found in the United States. The legs are stout and spiny, often modified for digging; the first

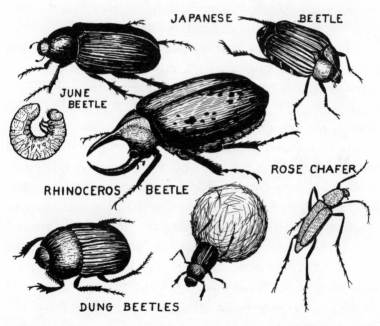

The Scarab Beetles number in their group many interesting insects, among them the familiar June Beetle, or June Bug, whose larvae are the destructive white grubs found in gardens.

- 85 -

segment of the thorax is exceptionally well developed, and in some species has a projecting horn or spine. The short antennae terminate in peculiar thin plates which resemble leaves of a book. A great number of species are plant-feeders, but there are other scarab beetles which are scavengers. In Egypt the scarab was held sacred as the symbol of immortality because, entering the soil, it seemed to die, then be resurrected. The scarab has long been a motif in Egyptian art.

Tumblebugs, or Dung Beetles, are dull black or metallic green scarabs about an inch in length. They have the interesting habit of chewing a piece of dung and working it into a ball, then rolling the ball to a suitable spot for burial in the ground. Sometimes several beetles will help each other in this task. The eggs are laid in the ball, and thus protected go through all the stages of metamorphosis, assured of an ample food supply.

June Beetles (also known as May Beetles and June Bugs) are brown scarabs abundant in northeastern United States in spring, when they congregate around lights. Adult June Beetles feed on leaves and flowers at night, and hide by day in the soil and among the roots of grasses. The larvae on the other hand are destructive white grubs which do great damage to lawns, pastures, and cereal crops by feeding on the roots. A relative, the Rose Chafer, is a slender, long-legged beetle of a pinkish tan color, which feeds on flowers and leaves of roses and other garden plants; its larva is also a white grub, destructive to roots.

Nursery stock coming from Japan introduced into this country one of our most serious scarab pests: the Japanese

Beetle. Originally discovered in New Jersey in 1916, it has now spread through a large part of eastern United States. The adult is brightly colored with greenish brown wings, dazzling green head and thorax, white-spotted abdomen. But its eating habits are not so pretty as, in hundreds, it swarms over flowers, leaves, and stems, leaving mutilated plants in its wake. The beetles live through winter as larvae in the soil.

Most grotesque—and also fearsome for such a small animal—is the eastern Rhinoceros Beetle, a dark brown beetle about an inch in length. The males have a single upright "horn" on the head. Species with two horns on the head occur in the South. Another southern resident is a large greenish gray species known as the Unicorn Beetle which grows to a length of two and a half inches.

STAG BEETLES, or PINCHING BUGS, are large shiny brown beetles whose males have overdeveloped mandibles which look like horns; in some species these powerful mandibles are half as long as the body. Stag Beetles prefer to live in the woods, but may be attracted to lights at night. The larvae are white grubs which live in rotting wood. Males often engage in mortal combat, fighting for the favor of a female who watches the fray from a safe distance.

The SNOUT BEETLES form an imposing assemblage of some 3000 American species, all intent upon getting their food from the same plants which we are growing for ourselves. These are small beetles, usually less than half an inch in length, in dull gray or brown colors. Their distinctive feature is a long curved beak, with small hidden mouth parts; the mandibles alone are visible at the tip of the beak. The legless white larvae with brown heads feed on roots and other underground parts of plants. As pupae the snout beetles sometimes encase themselves in silky cocoons. The list of agricultural pests among these beetles is a long one; it includes the Sweet Potato Weevil, the Cotton Boll Weevil, the Alfalfa Weevil, and the Billbugs.

The Sweet Potato Weevil is a fantastic-looking creature with blue-black wings and snout, reddish thorax, and ant-like appearance. It is common in the South where sweet potatoes are grown. The larvae bore into the vines and roots, and may not emerge from the sweet potatoes until after they are harvested. The Cotton Boll Weevil immigrated into this country from Mexico in 1890, and has spread throughout the cotton-growing states. The small yellowish brown adults feed on the seed pod, or boll, of the cotton plant and lay their eggs there; the larvae also feed on the boll and destroy the source of the cotton

Snout Beetles have peculiar elongated beaks; among them are many agricultural pests: Billbug (*left*), Sweet Potato Weevil (*center*), Cotton Boll Weevil (*right*).

fibers. Fortunately most adults die when hibernating; those that survive are usually kept in check by insect enemies, birds, and hot, dry weather. The Low-tide Billbug is an unusual insect in that it breeds in salt marshes along the Atlantic coast, being able in all stages to withstand daily submergence in salt water. The larvae tunnel into stems, the adults feed on parts of corn and pasture grasses above ground.

The Carnivorous Beetles

TIGER BEETLES are brilliantly colored insects of medium size (about half an inch in length), often metallic green or purple and sometimes striped, suggesting the common name. They like open sunlit habitats, and can be found on woodland paths and sandy beaches. Tiger beetles are swift runners with long agile legs. They eat a variety of insects which they capture with sickle-like mandibles capable of giving one a painful bite. The

Tiger Beetles (*left*) are brilliantly colored green or purple; their carnivorous larvae are known as doodlebugs. Stag Beetles (*right*) are large shiny brown beetles with enlarged horn-like mandibles in the males.

larvae are also active insect hunters; known as doodle-bugs, they live in vertical burrows in the ground and lie in wait with their heads and hungry jaws at the mouth of the burrow. A special hook-like appendage on one of the segments of the abdomen helps anchor the larvae in its burrow so firmly that it cannot be dislodged by a struggling victim. Tiger beetles spend the winter as larvae; when ready to go into the pupa stage they plug the entrance of their burrow and use it as a safe hiding place. The Six-spotted Tiger Beetle found in the woods is greenish blue with white spots along the forewing. A seashore species is white with black markings.

GROUND BEETLES. Most of these beetles are dark, shiny insects with elongated bodies and narrow heads, bearing powerful jaws. They grow to a length of an inch to an inch and a half. Most species are nocturnal, hiding under stones and logs by day and foraging for their prey at night. When in danger they prefer to run to safety rather than to fly. Many species eat caterpillars

Among the carnivorous beetles are the metallic-green Fiery Searcher (*right*) and the common Ground Beetle with blue-margined wings (*left*). Rove Beetles (*center*) are also insect hunters.

and thus as caterpillar hunters are a check on injurious moths. Ground beetles also eat snails, slugs, and earthworms. Some tear their prey apart and eat it piecemeal, others inject a digestive fluid into their victim and then suck in the food in liquid form. Adults survive winter by hibernating, and may live for several years. The eggs, laid in pits in the ground, hatch into larvae which spend their lives underground. Ground Beetles are themselves eaten by insectivorous rodents and birds. Species known as Bombardier Beetles have perfected their own type of chemical warfare. Glands near the tip of the abdomen discharge a volatile compound, with a popping sound. This substance changes to an irritating and vile-smelling cloud of vapor as it comes in contact with the air. Such equipment is undoubtedly good both for offense and defense. The Fiery Searcher is a large and colorful ground beetle of metallic green, so called because the liquid it gives off has a blistering effect. This beetle is one of the caterpillar hunters; it was introduced into this country from Europe to combat the gypsy moth.

ROVE BEETLES are another group of insect hunters. They have elongated, flattened bodies with broad heads and stout mandibles; most of the species are an inch or less in length. These beetles have the habit of running with the tip of the abdomen raised, like scorpions. They also depend upon gas warfare for defense; an alarmed rove beetle will face its enemy, aim its upraised abdomen forward, and shoot out a spray of irritating vapor. The Hairy Rove Beetle, a gray and black species, can be found around carrion, feeding on the scavenging insects which come to this type of food.

LADY BEETLES are also known as Lady Bugs and Ladybird Beetles. This group, with few exceptions, is a very helpful ally of man. These oval, convex, and brightly colored beetles are all small—half an inch or less in length. The tiny head is hidden beneath the first segment of the thorax. Common varieties are either red or yellow with black spots, or black with red or yellow spots. They feed on aphids, mealybugs, and scale insects; several Australian species have been introduced into this country to help fight the Citrus Mealybug and the Cottony-cushion Scale. The eggs are laid on plants where the insect food supply is likely to be found; the black and yellow larvae have the same appetite for aphids and scale insects as their parents. These beetles have long been esteemed as an ally in fighting injurious insects. In fact in the Middle Ages, the beetles were dedicated to the Virgin because of their help to man, and were known as "Beetles of Our Lady." Lady beetles have the unusual habit, for insects, of migrating in great

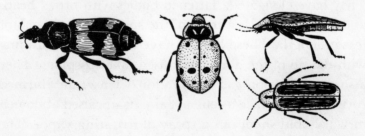

The Sexton Beetle (*left*) is dark brown or black; the Ladybird Beetle (*center*) is also known as the Ladybug; Fireflies are flattened beetles with velvety black or brown wings (*right*).

numbers to a hibernating place to spend the winter. In California these assemblages of lady beetles are collected, kept in cold storage, then sold to farmers at the proper season to control aphids.

CARRION BEETLES are dark brown or black beetles whose forewings do not cover the entire body; they are about an inch in length. The antennae terminate in club-shaped structures possessing thousands of olfactory pits, which aid the beetles in locating decaying flesh, on which they feed. Carrion beetles are also equipped with broad, spiny legs which function as digging tools. These little scavengers perform a necessary service in nature, in cleaning up the remains of dead animals. The Sexton Beetle, also called the Burying Beetle, is a particularly industrious scavenger capable of tackling such a large job as that of getting rid of a dead mouse. A pair of these beetles will set to work digging a hollow beneath the mouse and bury the remains in it. Eggs are laid in tunnels leading to this food supply; both young and adults can be assured of plenty to eat for many days.

FIREFLIES. Of all the unique activities of insects, by far the most striking is the blinking yellow lights of thousands of fireflies, or lightning bugs, as they gather in the twilight over a low meadow, or sparkle in the trees as darkness falls. Fireflies are elongated flattened beetles with velvety black or brown forewings, margined with a lighter color. During the day fireflies are inconspicuously hidden among grasses and weeds; it is said the adults do not feed at all. The eggs, laid in or on the ground, amid plants growing in damp locations, hatch into larvae with small heads and stout mandibles, which feed on earthworms, cutworms, and snails. In some species the females are wingless and look like larvae. Fireflies do no harm; in fact, the larvae often aid gardeners by reducing the number of snails and slugs.

Males, females, and larvae have luminous segments in the abdomen, of a yellowish green color; the females and larvae are sometimes called glow-worms for this reason. The males, in addition can give off intermittent bright flashes from these segments. The light of a firefly is unusual in being "cold"; all types of light used by man give off heat as well as light. Firefly light is produced by oxidation of a substance known as luciferin, whenever air is admitted; the firefly can control the supply of air coming to the segments via the tracheae. When a rich supply of air is present, an enzyme luciferinase makes possible instant oxidation of the luciferin. The lighting mechanism is a mating response, males and females using their lights as a mutual attraction.

Water-dwelling Beetles

WATER SCAVENGER BEETLES are large, oval, aquatic insects with brown or black wings and body; some reach a length of two inches. Adults are chiefly scavengers, but the larvae eat insects and other small aquatic animals. These beetles swim by moving their legs alternately; when they go underwater they carry an air supply with them on the underside of the body, trapped as a silvery film. The larvae breathe through gills on the abdominal segments. The pupa stage is spent on land, on or under the ground. Like most aquatic insects the adults can hibernate. Water Scavenger Beetles can fly well, and often are attracted to lights.

DIVING BEETLES. Ponds and quiet streams are the home of these shiny, dark colored beetles which might easily be mistaken for some of the aquatic bugs. They grow to a length of an inch or an inch and a half. Long hindlegs are flattened and hairy, thus useful as oars. Diving beetles float head downward with the tip of the abdomen above the surface film; the abdomen bears two large spiracles near its extremity and thus keeps the insect supplied with air. When diving underwater, the beetles carry a supply of air with them in a chamber under the forewings. At night diving beetles join other large aquatic bugs and beetles in congregating around lights. Adults live for several years, boring into the mud during winter. The fearless larvae, carnivorous as their parents, are sometimes fittingly called "water tigers." They inject a digestive juice into their prey which turns it into liquid; this nourishment the larvae take in through grooves on the inside of each curved mandible. Pupa

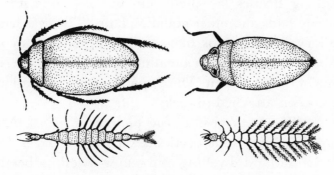

Diving Beetles (*left*, with larva) and Whirligig Beetles (*right*, with larva) are aquatic beetles feeding on other insects.

stages are spent on land, under logs and stones. Diving beetles are voracious feeders on other insects, snails, mussels, tadpoles, and salamanders. They do not hesitate to tackle fish much larger even than themselves; Diving beetles are in turn eaten by ducks, fish, and amphibians.

WHIRLIGIG BEETLES. The tireless merry-go-round activity of these black, oval beetles is familiar to anyone who has explored ponds and quiet pools. They seem to enjoy their continuous movement, interrupted only to pick up insects fallen into the water. The forelegs are modified for grasping food, the other two pairs of legs are short and flattened for swimming. A close look reveals that what, at first glance, looked like four compound eyes are instead two; this is the result of a division of each eye into an upper and a lower, usually submerged, portion. Adults give off a milky fluid with the smell of apples; they can also make a squeaking sound by rubbing the tip of the abdomen against the forewings. When these beetles dive, they carry a bubble of air with them. Whirligig Beetles lay their eggs on the underside of waterlily pads and other aquatic plants. The eggs hatch into larvae which look like small centipedes; they are equipped for underwater breathing with gills on the segments of the abdomen. The pupa stage occurs on land, in a cocoon attached to rocks or plants.

It is difficult to give a true picture of such a large group of insects as the beetles in only a few pages. Our selection of land-dwelling and water-dwelling beetles, some preying on other insects and some feeding on plants, will suggest what to look for next time you can get a close-up view of a beetle. As with the bugs, it is not just the appearance of the beetles which is intriguing; when you observe their activities, you will find still more to wonder at, in this strange world of insects.

Pupa of a Snout Beetle in repose

A Red-spotted Purple butterfly emerges from its pendant chrysalis.

CHAPTER SIX

THE SCALY-WINGED
INSECTS: BUTTERFLIES

Of all the insects, those in the order *Lepidoptera,* which
includes the butterflies and moths, have the greatest appeal. Theirs seems to be such a carefree existence as they
leisurely flit from flower to flower with airy grace. Their
beauty of form and color never fails to arouse admiration in even the least enthusiastic naturalist. Some are
very cosmopolitan, occurring in every state; others are
so rare that they can be found only on certain isolated
mountain tops. Of the 11,000 species in the order only
about 1,000 are butterflies; thus moths outnumber them
ten to one. Butterflies however seem more numerous because they are active by day and are more conspicuously
colored. Moths, for the most part, hide by day and fly
at dusk and night.

Wings of butterflies and moths are covered with tiny
scales which produce their color effects in one of two

ways. Some of the colors, as in many other animals, are pigments. But many of the colors are caused by minute parallel ridges on the surface of the scales which, like prisms, break up the light falling on them into its component shades. The iridescence typical of many butterflies is brought about by a thin transparent film which produces the same effect as the surface of a soap bubble. Color is often more than mere ornament. It may camouflage the insect by making it resemble its surroundings —the bark of a tree, the light and shadow of the woods, the dried fallen leaves. Color patterns also enable some species to mimic others. The Monarch butterfly for example has a bitter taste which makes it unpalatable to insect-eating animals; its colors identify it and give it immunity from attack. Another butterfly, the Viceroy, does not have this bad taste as a protection but its color pattern is so much like the Monarch's that it too is avoided by insect-eaters. The brilliant colors on the wings of some butterflies, which bring attention to the insect, suddenly vanish when these insects come to rest and fold their wings, showing the less conspicuously colored underside. Thus the pursuer loses track of his quarry.

The mouth parts of an adult butterfly or moth are highly specialized tools for sucking nectar from flowers. Mandibles are usually lacking, but the maxillae form a long hollow tongue—the proboscis—capable of penetrating deep into the throat of a flower. When not in use it is coiled like a watchspring beneath the head. Because of their flower-feeding habits, many species are useful pollinating agents. The upper end of the proboscis leads

A butterfly's wing is covered with tiny overlapping scales arranged like shingles on a roof.

into a bulb-like sac with muscular walls. As it contracts and expands, like the bulb in a syringe, it creates a vacuum which sucks nectar up through the tube. When the sac is full, a valve closes the opening to the proboscis, the muscular wall contracts again and forces the nectar into the stomach. In some species the adult lacks mouth parts and as a result can not eat. Since they may live only a few weeks, during this short period they can subsist on the excess food stored in the caterpillar before transformation into an adult.

Some adult Lepidoptera can hear by means of special resonating chambers or air sacs with tightly stretched membranes. The location of these auditory organs varies. They may be in the thorax, at the base of the hindwing; in the abdomen; or at the base of the wing veins. Their use is not well understood, for very few butterflies and moths can themselves make sounds. A notable exception is the Death's Head Moth which is able to produce a shrill chirping sound by forcing air through its proboscis. Caterpillars of this moth make crackling sounds by clicking their teeth together.

During the complete metamorphosis characteristic of this order, the eggs hatch into larvae which go through

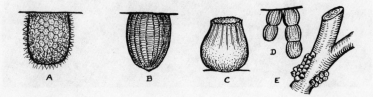

Butterfly eggs come in a variety of shapes: A, Viceroy; B, Monarch; C, Baltimore; D, Angle-wing; E, Mourning Cloak.

a resting stage or pupa before becoming adults. Most species have but one generation, or brood, a year, and live through winter as larvae or pupae. Some overwinter as eggs, and a very few as adults. Among the latter are two butterflies, the Monarch and the Mourning Cloak.

Few people associate caterpillars with particular kinds of butterflies or moths. Yet each species has its distinctive form, color, ornamentation and habits; many have special adaptations for protection, for moving about, and for getting their food. All are herbivorous and many are exceedingly destructive to garden and crop plants; the harmful species for the most part are caterpillars of moths. Butterfly caterpillars seem to be satisfied to munch on field and roadside flowers, shrubs and trees which are of little economic importance.

The cylindrical worm-like body of a caterpillar is

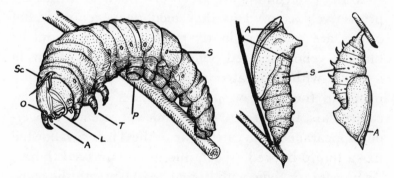

The cylindrical body of a caterpillar (Swallowtail, *left*) is divided into segments and bears two kinds of legs; the chrysalis may be supported by a silken girdle (Swallowtail, *left*) or may hang head-downward supported only by the tip of the abdomen (Fritillary, *right*).

– 103 –

noticeably divided into rings or segments. The first one is the small head, well protected by a chitinous covering and bearing six simple eyes and a mouth armed with powerful mandibles. With these cutting tools caterpillars can destroy leaves, sever stems of seedlings, bore into roots and wood, eat out the contents of seeds and fruits. The first three segments behind the head are the thorax; like the thorax of the adult, it bears three pairs of true legs, each with three horny sections and a single claw. The remaining segments of the body form a long abdomen which would drag on the ground if unsupported. This part of the body is provided with five additional pairs of legs, which enables the entire body to move smoothly over the surface. Lacking compound eyes and large antennae, caterpillars rely on sensitive feelers attached to the maxillae and lower lip to find their way around.

Many caterpillars are green or brown and thus are protectively colored as they feed on vegetation. But others are more brilliantly garbed, ranging from jet black to yellow and red. Some are as gaudy as clowns in a circus, with variegated costumes and grotesque ornaments in the form of spines and tufts of hair. A few caterpillars, though actually harmless, present a dangerous appearance. The caterpillar of the Tiger Swallowtail has a hump-backed aspect, due to an enlarged thorax. As it rests on a twig, with its real head beneath the body, this enlarged portion, marked by two conspicuous eyespots, resembles the head of a snake. Horns on the rear of the Wood-nymph caterpillar look like a forked tail. Other caterpillars have horn-like appendages on the head, sometimes directed forward in a menacing manner.

Molting takes place at regular intervals as the caterpillar grows. At these periods the larva stops feeding, splits the skin along its back, and crawls out, leaving the cast-off garment behind. This usually happens four or five times during the life of the caterpillar, the complete succession of molts taking two or three months. When their active feeding period is over, the larvae of butterflies attach themselves to the underside of a leaf or to a twig by means of a small button of silk. The silk comes from silk glands which are modified salivary glands, leading to an opening on the lower lip where the silk is extruded through a horny projection known as the spinneret. To this silky pad the caterpillar fastens its abdomen, and hangs head downward. The pupa of swallowtails adds the extra support of a silken girdle which holds its midsection to the twig, like an Indian papoose. The resting pupa becomes covered with a protective outer coat, through which various parts of the future adult can be distinguished. Such a pupa is known as a chrysalis. Most chrysalids are inconspicuously colored, green or yellow or brown. Some chrysalids remain in the resting stage for only a few weeks, others throughout the

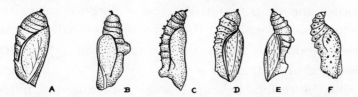

Butterfly chrysalids vary in appearance: A, Monarch; B, Viceroy; C, Tortoise; D, Buckeye; E, Question Mark; F, Regal Fritillary.

winter. It is a mystery even to scientists how these un-protected bits of delicate living matter can survive tem-peratures of fifty degrees below zero, as they do in the Arctic species, and then resume normal living activities in spring.

Butterflies differ from moths in many ways. The adult has a relatively slender body, compared with the hairy and stout thorax and abdomen of a moth. The antennae of butterflies usually end in tiny knobs, while those of moths are rarely knobbed and often fern-like or feathery. Butterfly wings are generally more brilliantly colored and held vertically above the body when at rest. The habits of the two groups are also different. Butterflies fly by day and are creatures of the sunlight, while most moths prefer the shadows and darkness of evening and night.

Their egg-laying habits also differ. Moth eggs are usually laid in clusters and coated with scales, hair, or a tough secretion. Butterfly eggs are more likely to be found, singly or in groups, arranged on the surface of leaves and stems without any special protection. The caterpillars of many moths are white or pale-colored, more like worms than most butterfly caterpillars; they also have adapted themselves more hungrily to eating garden and crop plants. A great difference is evident during metamorphosis: the pupa of a butterfly is rela-tively exposed, as a chrysalis, but that of a moth is often protected in a silken cocoon.

Our butterflies belong to some half dozen families, identified by entomologists on the basis of many techni-cal details. It is best for the beginner to rely upon identifying a few very common species and groups on the basis of size, colors, and shape of the wings. The following groups are arranged not so much by families as by possession of common form and colors to make such ready identification possible. Most easily recognized are the swallowtails, angle-wings, and tortoise-shells with their unusual wing margins and projections. The remaining butterflies, without such wing peculiarities, can be recognized by their colors, in a sequence from the white and yellow species, through those that are tan or brown or gray, to the dark-colored purple and blue butterflies. These are of course only a few of our many different kinds of butterflies, but an acquaintance with these members of the insect parade will be a good start at getting to know our butterfly neighbors.

The Swallowtails

Swallowtails are large butterflies, brilliantly colored and possessing several tail-like projections on each hindwing. The caterpillars are smooth skinned and have an enlarged thorax; some species have spines on the head. The chrysalis can be recognized by its peculiar method of attachment, being suspended by a silk girdle around the middle as well as by the abdominal pad. Swallowtails winter in the chrysalis stage.

TIGER SWALLOWTAIL. This, and the following Giant Swallowtail, are the largest species with a wingspread of five inches. The yellow and black striped wings have black margins, and those of the female are marked by a bluish area in the hindwings above the tail. Although most common in the middle Atlantic

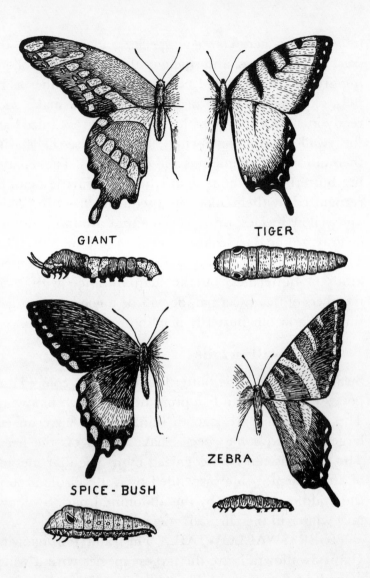

GIANT

TIGER

SPICE - BUSH

ZEBRA

Our largest and most gaily colored butterflies are found among the Swallowtails.

Coast states, it has a wide range at times from New England to Florida and west to Texas. A slightly smaller related species is found on the Pacific Coast. The caterpillar of the western variety feeds on alder and willow, that of the eastern one on cherry, birch and poplar.

GIANT SWALLOWTAIL. A native of the southern states, this bluish black butterfly can be recognized by the diagonal yellowish band in the forewing and the yellow spots along the margin of all four wings. The mottled yellow and brown caterpillar feeds on native trees of the rue family, such as prickly ash and hop tree. But with the introduction of orange and grapefruit trees of this same family, the caterpillar has transferred its attentions to these more abundant food supplies. It has become a pest in the Florida citrus groves, where it is known as the "orange puppy."

The SPICE-BUSH SWALLOWTAIL is a slightly smaller butterfly with a four-inch wingspread. It is a dusky member of the swallowtail clan, being blue-black with a row of lighter colored spots along the wing margins. This is a familiar species throughout the eastern and central states, where the caterpillar feeds on the aromatic foliage of spice-bush and sassafras. It makes little nests by drawing together the edges of leaves and fastening them with silk threads.

Also dark colored are the BLACK SWALLOWTAIL and the BLUE SWALLOWTAIL, with a three to four inch wingspread. The blue-black wings of the Black Swallowtail are marked with yellow and blue spots; this butterfly occurs everywhere in the eastern states. Its green striped caterpillar is also well known, and goes by the name of Parsley Worm because of its fondness for plants of this family. The Blue Swallowtail is also known as the Pipevine Swallowtail because of its preference for Dutchman's Pipe, a vine frequently grown to shade porches. This butterfly is a glossy blue-green with a brownish tinge to the forewings, with small whitish spots. The spiny caterpillar is a dusky brownish blue. Blue Swallowtails roam widely over eastern, central and southern United States, being found in as widely separated places as New England and the Grand Canyon in Arizona.

The ZEBRA SWALLOWTAIL is one of the midgets in the group, about three inches in wingspread. It is most abundant in the middle Atlantic states, but can be found from New England to the Rocky Mountains. The tails are very long and slender, and the black in the striped wings is more pronounced than in the Tiger Swallowtail. Its range is largely limited by the distribution of the pawpaw tree, on which the caterpillar feeds.

The Angle-wings.

These small to medium-sized butterflies are a warm reddish brown color, spotted with black. The coloring of the under surface of the wings often imitates the grays and the browns of bark and dead leaves. Angle-wings can be recognized by the unusual wing margin, which is scalloped or indented as if cut with scissors. Angle-wing caterpillars have slender hairy bodies, usually some shade of reddish or yellowish brown.

QUESTION MARK. With good imagination, you can interpret the silver crescent and spot on the underside of the hindwing as a question mark; hence the name. This is the largest angle-wing, with a wingspread of two and a half inches. The sickle-shaped forewings have a reddish tinge at their base, blending into a darker brown at the margins; large irregular dark spots mark both wings. The Question Mark is a very common butterfly, occurring throughout the United States except on the Pacific Coast. Its caterpillars feed on nettles and elm trees.

Slightly smaller is the SATYR, lighter in color, more distinctly spotted with black and with darker black margins. The caterpillars, like those of the Question Mark, prefer plants in the nettle family. Satyrs are western butterflies, living from the Rocky Mountain region to the Pacific Coast.

An angle-wing known as the FAUN, intermediate in size between the Satyr and the Question Mark, has the same reddish brown ground color and spotted wings. Both the Satyr and the Faun have a single small silvery

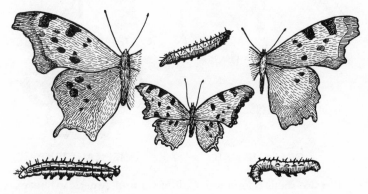

The Angle-wings include such common butterflies as the Question Mark (*left*), Satyr (*center*) and Faun (*right*).

– 111 –

crescent on the under surface of the hindwing. The deeply indented wing margins of the Faun give it an unkempt, tattered appearance. Its caterpillar feeds on willows. The Faun is a widespread species, found from New England to the Carolinas, west to the Pacific Coast.

The Tortoise-shells

Tortoise-shells are medium-sized butterflies of varying shades of brown and black, tinted with red and orange in such a fashion that their coloring reminds one of tortoise shell. The margin of the forewing is slightly scalloped, and the hindwing may have a slight projection. The COMPTON TORTOISE is a strikingly beautiful butterfly with irregular black spots in the forewings and

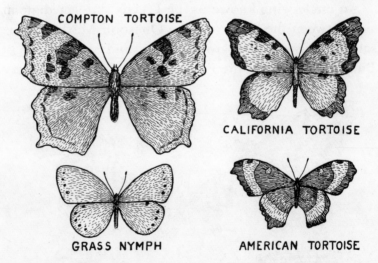

COMPTON TORTOISE

CALIFORNIA TORTOISE

GRASS NYMPH

AMERICAN TORTOISE

The Tortoise-shells (Compton, California and American) have red and orange tints which blend to give a tortoise-shell effect. In the Wood Nymph family we find the common Grass Nymph butterfly.

– 112 –

a single projection midway along the edge of the hind-wing; the total wingspread is about three inches. Its spiny caterpillar feeds on birches and willows. This species prefers the cool climate of the Pennsylvania mountains and the highland areas to the north. Like-wise found in the Appalachian region and in the states to the north and west, is the smaller AMERICAN TOR-TOISE with a two-inch wingspread. The wings are dark brown on the upper surface, with a broad yellowish band inside the margin of each wing and two orange-yellow spots near the middle of the front margin of the fore-wing. Intermediate in size is the CALIFORNIA TOR-TOISE, found from Colorado west to the Pacific Coast. It is marked somewhat like an angle-wing, with a dis-tinct black margin to each wing and heavy black spots along the forward edge of the forewing. The caterpillar feeds on elm, poplar and willow.

The Whites and The Sulphurs

We have all seen the numerous small white or yellow butterflies swarming around roadside puddles or over fields of clover. Many of them are only an inch in wing-spread. These light-colored butterflies belong to two groups, the one called the whites or cabbage butterflies, the other known as the sulphurs.

MUSTARD WHITE is a small butterfly, an inch and a half in wingspread, with a spotlessly white upper sur-face, but the under surface of the forewing is tipped with yellow and that of the hindwing is entirely yellow. It is a widely distributed species found throughout the United States. The familiar green caterpillar, common on cabbage plants, is marked with small black dots and has a narrow dark streak down its back.

The CHECKERED WHITE, a butterfly of the same size, occurs only east of the Rocky Mountains; its forewings are marked with several dark spots and at the front by a darker edge. The female wears a different costume, being buff-colored with whitish areas along the edges of both wings. The green caterpillar is striped with yellow and covered with small black warts. The WESTERN WHITE is a counterpart of the Checkered White, found in the western states; its forewing has a brownish leading edge, with spots of the same color on the upper surface of the forewing. The hindwing is a clear yellowish white.

These native species have been reduced in numbers by competition with an immigrant which arrived uninvited in Quebec about a hundred years ago, spread in a few years throughout New England and New York, and within thirty years had covered the country from coast to coast. This is the CABBAGE BUTTERFLY, whose caterpillar is the familiar Cabbage Worm. The adult,

Predominantly white butterflies are represented by the Great Southern White (*left*), the Cabbage Butterfly (*center*), and the Checkered White (*right*).

with a wingspread of an inch, is white with a dark brown edge to the front of the forewing, which is also marked with one or two dark spots. The smooth green caterpillar with pale lengthwise stripes has become the most destructive pest of the butterfly group, damaging great quantities of cabbage and cauliflower. This butterfly has been called the English sparrow of the insects.

GREAT SOUTHERN WHITE. With a wingspread of two inches, this is the largest member of the family. It may be either pure white, or yellowish white. In the male the front edge of the forewing alone is brownish, but both pairs of wings in the female have brown margins. The yellowish caterpillar is striped with dull blue and has bands of bright yellow. The Great Southern White, as its name suggests, is a tropical species which has found its way into the Gulf states.

The sulphurs are yellow butterflies, usually marked with brown margins and spots. The yellow caterpillars have small heads and bodies ornamented with crosswise rows of small warts; they feed on peas, beans, clover and other plants in the pea family. Throughout the United

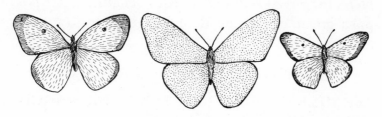

Among the yellow butterflies are the Orange Sulphur (*left*), Cloudless Sulphur (*center*) and Common Sulphur or Alfalfa Butterfly (*right*).

States ranges the CLOUDLESS SULPHUR, whose wings measure slightly more than two inches across. The males are an attractive pure yellow, but the females have brown wing margins and a spot in the center of each wing. Cloudless Sulphurs are very common among Florida orange groves.

The ORANGE SULPHUR is smaller, with an inch and a half wingspread. Although it occurs in the East and the South, it is most abundant in the West. The male is yellow with dark wing margins, dark spots in the forewings, and a reddish spot in each hindwing. The females may be either white or yellow, with a broad dark margin and more conspicuous spots.

COMMON SULPHUR. Also known as the Alfalfa Butterfly, this sociable little yellow butterfly likes to sit with its companions around puddles and wet mudholes, sipping the water. The male is yellow with a brown edge to the wing margins, a dark spot in each forewing and a lighter spot in each hindwing. The females may be either white or yellow. Common Sulphurs can be found anywhere east of the Rocky Mountains; they often gather in great numbers in clover and alfalfa fields. Here the green caterpillar, with lengthwise stripes of paler green, can get its fill of foliage, often to the farmers' loss.

The Milkweed Butterfly and Its Mimic

The MILKWEED BUTTERFLY, or MONARCH, is undoubtedly our best known butterfly, being found everywhere in the United States. It has gained fame also as a world traveler, having crossed the seas to establish itself in such faraway places as Australia and the Philippines. It is a reddish brown butterfly, three or four inches across the wings, with conspicuous black veins and wing margins. It is avoided by hungry insect-eaters because of its acrid secretions, making it a disagreeable morsel. Monarch butterflies are among the few insects which migrate. In autumn, from coast to coast, they begin congregating in flocks, flying southward by day and roosting in the trees by night, until they reach the milder climate of the southern states, from Florida to California. The females lay their eggs on milkweed, so when they hatch the caterpillars feed on this plant. Monarch caterpillars are smooth and greenish yellow, banded with black; threadlike horns at both ends of the body wave excitedly when the larva is disturbed.

The QUEEN is a slightly smaller relative of the Monarch, of rich brown color and with the same dark margins to the wings, which however lack the black veins. Its caterpillar likewise feeds on milkweed. The Queen can be found from the Gulf states westward to Arizona.

VICEROY. This butterfly has the same coloring and general appearance as the Monarch, and is about the same size. But a close look at the hindwing reveals a slight difference: the Viceroy has an extra black line crossing the vein pattern of the hindwing. This minor variation seems to escape birds and other insect-eaters, for they give the Viceroy as wide a berth as they do the vile-tasting Monarch, even though the Viceroy lacks the bitter taste. Thus the mimicry happens to be of great value to the Viceroy. The chunky larva is mottled green and white, with horns on the head end; it feeds on willows, poplars and aspens. When there are two broods a year, the caterpillar of the autumn brood rolls itself up in a cradle made by tying together the edges of a leaf with silken threads and lining the interior with silk. Here it hibernates for the winter, completing its metamorphosis in early spring when food again becomes available. The Viceroy occurs throughout the United States east of the California Sierras.

The Fritillaries

Fritillaries are medium-sized to large butterflies with a bewildering number of species, many of them so alike that accurate identification is difficult. Their general color is some shade of brown; this is marked with spots,

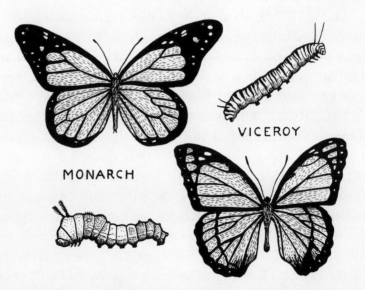

VICEROY

MONARCH

The Viceroy mimics the appearance of the slightly larger Monarch; both are brownish butterflies marked with black.

– 118 –

bars and crescents of black. The under-surface of some fritillaries is so beautifully decorated with silvery spots that these species are known also as Silverspots. An unusual trait of the caterpillars is that most of them feed only at night, and restrict their eating to violets. Among the adults of some species the males and females are of such different colors that they might easily be mistaken for different kinds of butterflies. Two of the largest fritillaries, with wingspreads of three to four inches, are the Regal Fritillary and the Great Spangled Fritillary. Among the smallest is the Silver-bordered Fritillary, only an inch and a half across the wings. The others are intermediate in size.

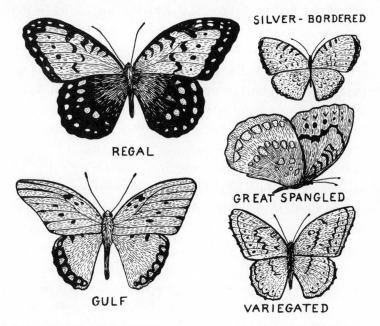

SILVER-BORDERED

REGAL

GREAT SPANGLED

GULF

VARIEGATED

Many of the speckled Fritillaries are marked with silver spots on their under-surface.

REGAL FRITILLIARY. This butterfly lives up to its name, for it is a beautifully marked, iridescent species with yellowish brown forewings, margined in darker brown, and olive-brown hindwings spotted with white. On the under-surface are numerous silvery spots and crescents. The Regal Fritillary is most common in swampy meadows and open glades in the woods, near violets and milkweeds; its range is from New England to Nebraska. The black larvae are striped with orange-red and armed with bristly spines.

GREAT SPANGLED FRITILLARY. This large butterfly is common throughout eastern and central United States; its name refers to the spangled appearance of the under surface of the hindwing, which is decorated with many large silvery spots. The upper surface of the wings is yellowish brown, covered with dark spots and blotches. The black spiny caterpillars have the unusual habit of hibernating soon after they have hatched, having eaten nothing but the remains of their eggshells. The following spring they emerge and complete their development when food becomes abundant.

There are many kinds of medium-sized fritillaries. The VARIEGATED FRITILLARY is light yellowish brown, marked by darker spots but without silvery spots on the under-surface of the wings. This is a southern species, common from Virginia southward and westward. The reddish yellow larvae with lengthwise brown stripes along the side and white spots on the back, likes to feed on passion flower vines. Another southern species is the GULF FRITILLARY, a uniformly light-brown butterfly with a few spots on the forewing and a dark margin to the hindwing; the underside bears silvery spots. The caterpillar of this species also feeds on passion flower vines. From Ohio westward we find the RUDDY SILVERSPOT, a small fritillary with dark cinnamon-brown hindwings with the usual spots, and a silver-spotted under-surface. In California an abundant species is the CALLIPE, a fritillary with dusky brown wing bases blending into yellow at the outer edges. Its upper surface is heavily marked with black, its under surface is grayish green speckled with silver.

Peacock Butterflies

These medium-sized butterflies, about two inches in wingspread, are dusky gray or brown with striking eye-spots like those of a peacock's wing. A common species is known as the BUCKEYE, found in the southern states. Each forewing has a whitish band, with a single large eyespot, and smaller orange-red spots along the forward edge of the wing. Each hindwing bears two eye-spots just inside a small reddish band. The dark gray

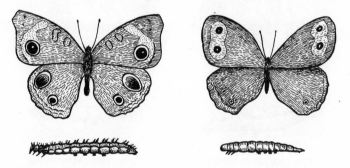

The Buckeye (*left*) has peacock-like "eyes" on its wings, as does the more sedate Wood Nymph, or Grayling (*right*).

caterpillars, marked with yellow stripes and purple spines, feed on plantain.

Wood-nymphs and Satyrs

As their name suggests, these butterflies are creatures of the shady woods and open forest glades; the mouse-gray of the upper surface of the wings is a contrast to the more colorful under surface. Eyespots occur on the wings, but are smaller than those of the peacock butterflies.

The familiar WOOD-NYMPH or GRAYLING has a wingspread of less than two inches. A yellow area in each forewing bears two conspicuous eyespots which may have a blue center. The females leave their shaded retreats to lay their eggs on grasses in fields, for the cater-

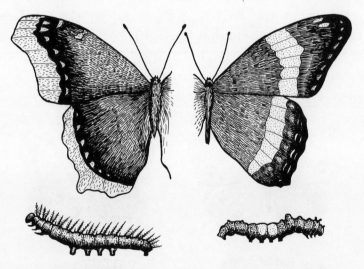

Among the purplish-black butterflies are the Mourning Cloak (*left*) with yellow-edged wings, and the Banded Purple (*right*) with white bands across its wings.

– 122 –

pillars are grass eaters. The smooth reddish or brownish caterpillars are thickest in the middle and taper at each end; the abdomen terminates in a pair of diverging horns which give the animal the appearance of having a forked tail. Much larger, with a wingspread of almost three inches, is the SOUTHERN WOOD-NYMPH, which looks like the common Wood-nymph except for a broader yellow band on the under surface of the forewing. Its range is throughout the Gulf states. The GRASS-NYMPH is a small northeastern species, found as the common name indicates in the more open and sunny locations of grassy fields. The dull-brown wings are marked by several dark eyespots near the margin, with larger eyespots on the under surface.

The Purples and Hairstreaks

Only a few of our common butterflies are dark in color, with shades varying from blue and purple to black. The most familiar member of this group is the MOURNING CLOAK, found throughout the United States. The purplish black wings reach a wingspread of three inches; each wing is edged with bright yellow, inside of which

The Great Purple Hairstreak (*left*) and the Colorado Hairstreak (*right*) are richly colored blue and purple butterflies.

is a single row of blue spots and crescents. This is another of the few butterflies which hibernates as an adult. As a result it is one of the first butterflies to add color to the woods in early spring, often while the deciduous trees are still leafless. The female encircles the twig of a willow with her egg clusters; these hatch into ornate caterpillars, black with orange-red spots and rows of spines. The larvae feed on poplar and elm, as well as on willow.

The BANDED PURPLE is a butterfly of about the same size but with a range restricted to the northeastern states. It is readily recognized by the dark wings of brownish purple, banded in white. Each hindwing may have reddish spots at its base. Caterpillars of the Banded Purple feed on birch and willow. The related RED-SPOTTED PURPLE has black wings, blending into blue at the margin; the under surface of the wings is brown with red spots. This butterfly occurs throughout the United States east of the Rocky Mountains. Its caterpillar seems dressed for a costume party, with a variegated body of cream, green and brown. Two large horn-like spines on the enlarged thorax give the caterpillar a fearsome aspect. Its food is chiefly wild cherry and willow.

Our most tropical-looking butterflies belong to the hairstreaks, many of which are richly colored in blue. The GREAT PURPLE HAIRSTREAK, which is found from Florida to California, is an iridescent blue-green butterfly with a brown margin to the wings; the under surface is brown with crimson wing-bases. The hindwings bear a long slender tail, like a miniature swallow tail. Caterpillars of the Purple Hairstreak feed on mistletoe, a leafy parasite of oaks in the southern states. In the far west occurs the COLORADO HAIRSTREAK, a royal purple butterfly with dark wing margins and an oblique black band on each forewing, and with orange spots on the hind edge of the wings.

This review of the butterflies in our insect parade can give us but a glimpse of the numerous and colorful members of the thousand species found in the United States. You already knew, I am sure, the Tiger Swallowtail, Cabbage Butterfly, Monarch and Viceroy, the Fritillaries and the Mourning Cloak. To this small number of very familiar butterflies we have added some other common and interesting butterflies. You may discover many others not described in this chapter. To identify all the kinds you are likely to encounter if you go butterfly-hunting, you will have to use the butterfly guide books of which a few are suggested in the Afterword.

Artificial "eyes" adorn the sides of the body, behind the head, of the Swallowtail caterpillar and give it a ferocious aspect

The Sphinx moth is equipped with a long tongue which is neatly coiled when not in use.

CHAPTER SEVEN

THE SCALY-WINGED
INSECTS: MOTHS

Moths are fascinating insects for several reasons. They have an elusive habit of appearing like phantoms out of the night, fluttering at our lighted windows, and then disappearing silently into the darkness. The delicate pastel shades of their attire are a contrast to the gaudy brilliance of many butterflies. For the more practical minded they are useful animals because of their unique silk-manufacturing ability which resulted in the domestication of the silkworm moth over 4,000 years ago. Whatever the cause, the capture of a large moth is always an exciting event among young naturalists.

Moths, as we have seen, differ from butterflies in many ways. In only a few instances, as in the case of the male Promethea Moth and the Ailanthus Moth which fly by day, is one likely to confuse a moth with a butterfly. Most moths have stout hairy bodies which often seem unusually large and clumsy compared to the small narrow wings. Some moths look much like bumblebees or hummingbirds for this reason. Most moths also have plume-like antennae rather than clubbed or knobbed ones. Many moths use their silk glands for a variety of purposes. Some construct community shelters of silk webbing as we see in the tent caterpillar. Others make little cases or homes for themselves of the silk; a familiar example of this is in the bagworm moths. Some caterpillars, when disturbed while feeding, drop from a leaf to the ground but spin behind them a silken lifeline on which they climb back to the leaf when danger is over. Moth caterpillars are best known, perhaps, for their habit of making cocoons, each a silken cradle in which the final stages of metamorphosis take place. In the silkworm moths so much silk is spun in the cocoon that these moths have for centuries been the source of this valued textile fiber.

In only a few of the many families of moths are the adults conspicuous in size and coloring; these however are very beautiful and some are larger than butterflies. The majority of moths have developed camouflaging colors and patterns, and try their best to be inconspicuous; these are small, light-colored insects, hiding by day and difficult to see at night. Most of the adults have no common names, but are called by the names of their caterpillars since these are familiar as agricultural pests. The large colorful moths are found among the giant silkworm moths, the royal moths, and the sphinx moths; smaller but conspicuously colored species occur in the tiger moth and underwing moth groups. Of the many inconspicuous but economically important moth families, our insect parade includes the clothes moth, codling moth, tussock

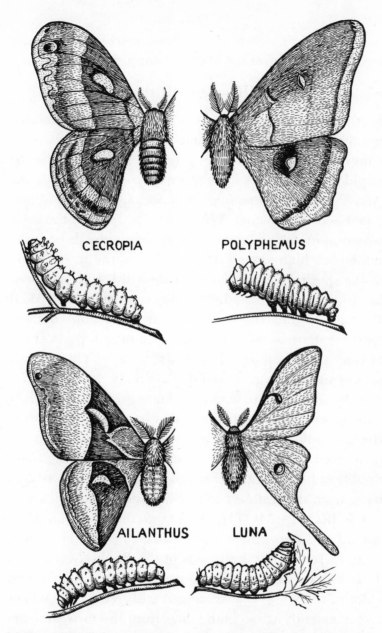

CECROPIA

POLYPHEMUS

AILANTHUS

LUNA

Moths attain their greatest size in the Giant Silkworm Moth family; the Cecropia has a wingspread of seven inches.

moth groups as well as the families in which bagworms, webworms, inchworms, and tent caterpillars occur.

The Giant Silkworm Moths

Moths attain their greatest size in this family of conspicuously beautiful species. Our Cecropia Moth with a wingspread of seven inches is really a giant among the Lepidoptera. But even it is small compared with the Atlas Moth of southeastern Asia which measures almost a foot across the wings. With a few exceptions, the giant silkworm moths are night fliers, spending the days sitting motionless high among the branches of the trees. Many of the species are the source of the wild silks produced in Asia and the East Indies; the true Silkworm Moth belongs to a different family. An unusual feature of these moths is that the adult has either no mouth parts at all, or ones so incomplete that it can not eat. Thus it lives on the surplus food material in its body, left over after transformation from a pupa. The caterpillar has had enough to eat, not only for its own needs, but for use in the later adult stage. Winter is spent as a pupa, protected in a silken cocoon with a tough outer covering. You doubtless have noticed these cocoons in winter, as they hang from the leafless twigs or lie among fallen leaves.

CECROPIA MOTH. This large moth, with a wingspread of seven and a half inches, can be found from May to July in the states east of the Rocky Mountains. It is known also as the Emperor Moth. The ground color of the wings is gray, tinged with red; a wavy light streak extends across both wings from the forward margin of the forewing to the rear margin of the hindwing. Near the base of each wing is a large crescent-shaped spot of white and red, bordered in black. The body is bright red, with white bands on the abdomen. A Cecropia caterpillar reaches four inches in length; its greenish body is decorated with rows of tubercles, blue ones on the sides, yellow ones on the back, and additional red ones on the thorax. It feeds on maple, elm, cherry and apple but its appetite is not great enough to do any damage. The large cocoons (up to four inches in length) are attached to twigs by their side; they are often discovered and eaten by squirrels and woodpeckers.

POLYPHEMUS MOTH. Almost as large as the Cecropia, this tawny yellow moth has a large black and

A close-up view of the Polyphemus moth reveals a hairy body and legs, and marvelously intricate feathery antennae.

blue spot in each hindwing, a smaller transparent spot in each forewing. The hindwing also has a dark line inside its margin, while the forewing has a similar but lighter-colored marking. Polyphemus Moths are found throughout the United States, being various shades of cream, brown, or red in different parts of the country. Like the Cecropia, it is active from May to July. The short, chunky caterpillar is bright green with a brown head; its body, pleated like an accordion, is studded with little red buttons. It feeds on a number of different trees, but can generally be found on oak and birch. To intimidate an enemy this caterpillar has the startling habit of elevating the front part of its body, pulling in its head, and clicking its jaws. Studies on this species give a revealing picture of the tremendous appetite of caterpillars. During a two month period, a Polyphemus caterpillar consumed 86,000 times its original weight in food, and increased its weight 4,000 times! After such a feeding orgy, the caterpillar is ready to take a rest as a pupa, inside an ovoid cocoon attached to a leaf. When the leaf dies and falls to the ground, the cocoon falls with it, wintering among the leaves on the ground.

The AILANTHUS MOTH, in markings and size, is much like a Cecropia, but is olive-green with narrower wings. This is an introduced moth, brought to the United States in 1861 in the hope of using it for silk production. The silk of the cocoon however is rather coarse, and no satisfactory method was found for reeling it. Now the Ailanthus Moth can be found along the Atlantic Coast in a wild state. Being one of the few day-flying moths it can easily be mistaken for a large greenish yellow butterfly. The moth gets its name because the caterpillar feeds on ailanthus trees. Its cocoon is wrapped in a leaflet, attached to the twig by silken cords.

Smaller than the preceding, with a three-inch wing-spread, the PROMETHEA MOTH, or SPICE-BUSH MOTH, is found throughout eastern United States. It is more frequently encountered than its larger relatives. This is one of the few moths with a color difference between the males and the females. The male is black, with putty-colored wing margins, while the more colorful female is reddish and marked somewhat like a Cecropia by a wavy streak across the wings and a light-colored crescent-shaped spot in each wing. Active during mid-summer, the males fly only in the daytime, the females at night. The caterpillar is fond of spice-bush, but it also feeds on sassafras, tulip trees and wild cherry. The cater-pillar looks much like that of a Cecropia, only smaller. The leaf-wrapped cocoons are fastened to twigs by silken cords which hold fast all winter. Thus the dangling cocoons are easily seen when the branches are leafless.

LUNA MOTH. If moths were to stage a beauty contest, the Luna Moth would be acclaimed queen without any near rivals. The delicate green coloring, the symmetry of the wings with their long graceful tails, give this moth breath-taking grace. The forward margin of the forewing has a rich brown edge, and each wing has a dainty eyespot. Although large (it has a wingspread of three to four inches) and found over a large range from Maine to Florida and Texas, the Luna Moth is less frequently seen than the Cecropia or Polyphemus because of its habit of flying from late night until dawn, rather than from twilight to early evening. It also prefers the woods to open fields and suburban country. Its flight is a peculiar up-and-down dancing movement, near the outer branches of trees, rather than the swooping and darting of other large moths. The caterpillars resemble those of Polyphemus but the head is green instead of brown and the body segments are marked with narrow white bands. They feed on a number of trees but are often found on walnut, hickory, sweet gum, persimmon and oak. The thin-walled cocoon of silk and leaves falls to the ground and spends the winter among the dead vegetation.

Two small moths belong to the same group as these large silkworm moths. The IO MOTH has a wingspread of two inches; both sexes have yellow hindwings but the forewing of the female is yellowish brown while that of the male is yellow. Each hindwing is marked by a large and conspicuous dark eyespot. The green caterpillar has a reddish stripe on each side and bears a number of spines. Because these are connected with small poison

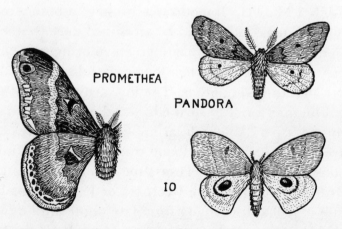

PROMETHEA

PANDORA

IO

Smaller members of the Giant Silkworm Moth family are the Promethea, Pandora and Io Moths.

glands which can cause an uncomfortable sting, this caterpillar should be handled with care. Io Moths are found over a wide territory from Maine to Florida and west to the Rio Grande River. The caterpillars feed on a variety of vegetation from clover to trees. The PANDORA MOTH, of the same size as the Io Moth, is common to the Rocky Mountain region. Its forewings are dark grayish brown, the hindwings are lighter colored with a rosy tint at their base. Each wing has a small spot near the center. The caterpillars have a taste for ponderosa pine, and at times are a threat to these valuable timber trees. Strange as it may seem, the larvae are dried and stewed by the Indians of the Southwest.

The true SILKWORM MOTH is a close relative to the Giant Silkworm Moths; it is an Asiatic species which has been domesticated in China and Japan. The silkworm is considered the most beneficial of all insects. Adults are creamy white moths of small size, with hairy bodies and short weak wings. They do not eat, rarely fly, and live only for a few days, just long enough to mate, lay eggs and perpetuate the race. Each female lays 300–400 eggs which hatch into naked caterpillars about three inches in length. These feed on mulberry leaves and become full grown at the end of six weeks. As they prepare for the pupa stage they construct a cocoon lined with a single silk thread a thousand feet long. The secret of the silkworm's achievement lies in two large silk glands which produce a clear sticky liquid that hardens into a fiber when exposed to the air. A silken filament passes from each gland to the spinneret on the underlip, where the two strands are fused to form one silken thread. Moving its head around in a regular rhythm, the caterpillar spends three days in spinning the thread of its cocoon. When the silkworm is raised for commercial silk production, the pupa is killed when it has finished its task for if it lived to break through the cocoon it would sever the thread. The thread is reeled off from each cocoon and used in making the finished silk; one pound of silk requires the labors of 25,000 caterpillars!

The Royal Moths

These large moths are closely related to the giant silkworm moths, but lack the transparent spots on the forewings. The caterpillars are distinguished for the single long spine on the ninth abdominal segment. They do not spin cocoons but instead burrow into the ground and spend the winter as unprotected chrysalids.

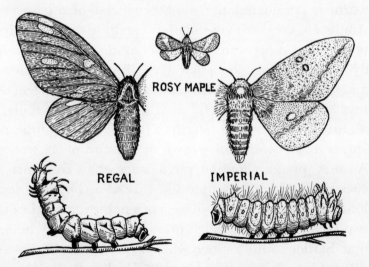

The Royal Moth family includes the Imperial and the Rosy Maple Moths as well as the Regal, or Royal Walnut, Moth whose caterpillar is known as the Hickory Horned Devil.

The ROYAL WALNUT MOTH, or REGAL MOTH, has a five-inch wingspread; the forewings are olive gray, spotted with yellow, and the veins are heavily marked with red. This large moth is common in the Atlantic Coast states but is not as frequently encountered as its ferocious-looking caterpillar known as the Hickory Horned Devil. This grotesquely spined larva, four to five inches in length, has long curved spines at the head end, smaller spines on other segments of the body. In spite of its appearance it is entirely harmless. It feeds on hickory, walnut, and persimmon trees. Also of large size, with a wingspread up to five inches, is the IMPERIAL MOTH. This is a yellow moth with spots and wing margins of rose-purple, found over a wide range. The green, brown and black hairy caterpillar feeds on pines and other trees. The ROSY MAPLE MOTH, a small relative in a royal family, has a wingspread of only an inch and a half; its wings are banded in yellow and pink. The striped caterpillar feeds on maples, and often becomes a pest on silver maple trees in cities. This species is most abundant in the mid-western states.

The Sphinx Moths

The sphinx-like position assumed by the caterpillars, as they hunch the forward portion of their bodies, is responsible for one common name of these moths. They are also appropriately known as Hawk Moths because of their large bodies and swift flight. Some can hover over a flower like a hummingbird, for which a hawk moth can easily be mistaken. Viewed from above, the rapidly tapering narrow wings and spindle-shaped body give these moths the outlines of fighter planes. Some species can fly as fast as 35 miles per hour. Sphinx Moths are of medium to large size, and include a number of common species. A few lack scales and thus have transparent wings, but the majority are varicolored. Moths of this family have a long proboscis; this is unusually prominent in the Giant Sphinx. Both night and day fliers occur in the group. The large green caterpillars are known as hornworms because of a large horn on the eighth segment of the abdomen. This horn is harmless but when thrashed about by an excited caterpillar its appearance is sufficient to scare away an inquisitive bird. Adult Sphinx Moths are helpful in pollinating garden plants; only a few of the caterpillars are injurious to crops.

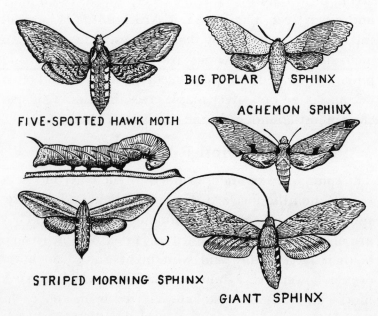

BIG POPLAR SPHINX

FIVE-SPOTTED HAWK MOTH

ACHEMON SPHINX

STRIPED MORNING SPHINX

GIANT SPHINX

Sphinx Moths are stream-lined fast-flying moths; many of the species are known as Hawk Moths.

The FIVE-SPOTTED HAWK MOTH is a grayish green moth of four-inch wingspread whose forewings look like watered silk. The hindwings are gray with irregular black bands parallel to the wing margin. The abdomen is conspicuously marked with orange-red spots on either side. The large green caterpillars feed on tomato plants to such an extent that it is known as the Tomato Hornworm. In the southern states, where this moth is abundant, the caterpillars are called appropriately by still another name—the Tobacco Hornworm—because it is such a pest on tobacco plants. These caterpillars can be recognized by the single horn near the end of the abdomen, and by the diagonal light stripes on the side.

The GIANT SPHINX, with a five-inch wingspread, is the largest of the family. It is a tropical species which ventures into Florida and the Gulf states. Olive-green in color, the forewings are mottled and the hindwings have a yellowish tint at their base. Giant Sphinx caterpillars feed on plants in the pawpaw family.

Many of the sphinx moths are of medium size, two to three inches in wingspread. The BIG POPLAR SPHINX is a dainty moth found throughout the United States, pale blonde with tints of gray and rose in the small hindwing. Western varieties of this moth are of lighter shades than the eastern ones, blending with the tan and gray of the prairie and desert country. Caterpillars of this species feed on willows and poplars. The ACHEMON SPHINX, also found throughout the United States, has tan-colored forewings with several dark spots, and hindwings of a rosy hue with a tan margin. The red or green caterpillars, when full grown, lose the horn typical of other hornworms. The segments near the head form loose folds so that the caterpillar can draw in its head when alarmed. Their food consists of grape vines and Virginia creeper. The STRIPED MORNING SPHINX is a very common species, occurring throughout the country. It is active at every hour of the day and night and never seems to rest. We can find this little sphinx moth in bright sunshine at midday, and also around street lights at night. The olive-gray forewings each have a diagonal light-colored band; the hindwings are darker colored, with a rosy band. Adults congregate around thistles to sip their nectar, while the caterpillars feed on spring beauty and other plants in the purslane family.

Tiger Moths

Adult tiger moths are small brown or orange moths, sometimes spotted or banded; they are nocturnal and not as often encountered as their familiar caterpillars, the woolly-bears. The ISABELLA TIGER MOTH measures about an inch across the yellowish brown wings, which have small spots scattered over the upper surface. The abdomen bears three rows of black dots. The caterpillars wear a thick hairy coat, black at each end and brown in the middle. Known as Banded Woolly-bears, they have a reputation in some localities as prophets of how cold the coming winter will be, depending upon the width of the brown saddle. There is no scientific evidence as to their prophetic accuracy. It is in their favor, however, that their chief food consists of weeds. The Brown Woolly-bear found on cultivated plants is the caterpillar of the SALT MARSH MOTH, which feeds on grasses. The adult female has all-white wings with a few small spots, while the male has hind-wings which are entirely yellow. The FALL WEB-WORM, found throughout the United States, is a social-minded caterpillar which likes to live in tent-covered communities on cherry, ash, and maple. Its silken webs cover the entire branch and thus differ from those of the tent caterpillar, usually constructed around a fork in a branch. The moths are white, sometimes spotted with black.

Underwings and Their Relatives

These comprise one of the largest families of the Lepidoptera. Among them are many of the common night-flying moths attracted to lights. Many of the species can be recognized by their threadlike antennae, the broad hindwings which are often differently colored from the forewings. The smooth-skinned and dull-colored caterpillars eat foliage, cut plant stems, and destroy fruits; some of these are known as cutworms. In contrast to the grubs of beetles, cutworms can be recognized by having fleshy legs on the abdomen.

The BLACK WITCH is the most impressive moth of

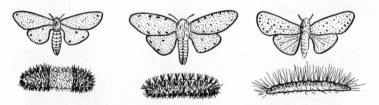

The Isabella Tiger Moth (*left*) is best known for its brown and black Woolly Bear larva; the Salt-marsh Moth (*center*) has an entirely brown Woolly Bear; the Fall Webworm is the hair caterpillar of another kind of Tiger Moth (*right*).

– 141 –

the group, its four-inch wingspread setting it apart from the other smaller moths. The dark brown wings are variegated with black, and a wavy whitish band extends from the front edge of the forewing to the rear edge of the hindwing. The native home of this species is tropical America but it often appears in the southern states, occasionally venturing as far north as New York. The caterpillar feeds on plants in the pea family.

The underwings are attractive moths with a striking difference between the neutral-colored forewings and the more colorful hindwings. The WHITE BIRCH UNDERWING lives in the northeastern states, where white and gray birches are common. When at rest on the bark of a birch tree, the mottled white and gray forewings, folded over the hindwings, camouflage the moth beautifully. In flight the moth reveals its olive-green hindwings with white margin and white band. This moth has a wingspread of several inches. The DARLING UNDERWING, found in the Appalachian Mountain region, has mottled dark gray forewings which likewise camouflage this species as it rests on the trunks of maple trees. Its dark brown hindwings are marked with two broad red bands on each wing. A similar but smaller underwing with black and red banded hindwings occurs

The White Birch Underwing (*left*) and Darling Underwing (*right*) have neutral-colored forewings and colorful banded hindwings.

in the western states. Underwing caterpillars feed on willows and poplars.

Many members of this family are destructive as caterpillars. The BLACK CUTWORM is the larval stage of a sooty colored moth about two inches in wingspread. This is the familiar dark cutworm which coils up, head to tail, when disturbed. Hibernating underground until spring, as soon as seedlings appear so does this greedy little caterpillar, ready to cut down tender tomato and potato plants. The ARMYWORM is the larval stage of another moth, with light brown wings and a white spot in the middle of each forewing. The dark-gray caterpillars are marked with lengthwise yellow stripes on their back, and a wider yellowish green stripe along the sides. They feed on grasses and cultivated species in the grass family, such as corn and wheat. Their habit of traveling from one feeding ground to another in great numbers gives them the name of armyworm. Caterpillars of a dark brown moth, about an inch and a half in wingspread with a silvery spot in each forewing, are known as CABBAGE LOOPERS because of their habit of moving by inching along, as measuring worms do. This

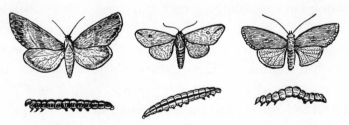

Other members of the Underwing family are the destructive Black Cutworm (*left*), Armyworm (*center*) and Cabbage Looper (*right*).

type of locomotion is necessary because the larvae have only three pairs of legs on the abdomen. They progress by stretching forward, planting the thoracic legs on firm ground, then arching their backs and bringing the abdominal legs forward.

Some Moths With Notorious Larvae

Many families of moths have made themselves obnoxious by having larvae which feed on articles of clothing, rugs, stored foods and other household goods as well as on ornamental and crop plants. The identification and control of these pests is a complete science in itself, and requires employment of thousands of entomologists by the state and federal governments. We can mention only a few of the most destructive species, but every reader will be able to think of others which he has come across in the home and the garden, and in the farmers' fields.

The "moth millers" which fly out of clothes closets and head for dark corners in which to hide are narrow-winged, tan or light-colored moths with fringed wings and less than an inch of wingspread. They lay tiny eggs on fabrics which are destined to be food for the larvae; these are small caterpillars with an outsized ability to eat holes in rugs, clothing and draperies. The WEBBING CLOTHES MOTH has yellowish forewings, pale hindwings, with long fringed margins. Hiding in a fold of material while feeding, the larva eventually spins itself a cocoon of silk mingled with fibers from the cloth. The CASE-MAKING MOTH is another "moth miller" with shiny yellowish brown forewings, variegated with brown, and lighter unspotted hindwings, both fringed as in the Webbing Moth. The larva constructs a cylindrical case as its home, enlarging it with fibers taken from the material on which it is feeding, lining the interior with silk. By fall its growth is complete and the larva rests for the winter in its case. In spring it becomes a pupa and soon emerges as a moth, ready to do more damage by laying eggs in fresh feeding grounds.

The bagworm moths, in spite of their destructive habits in stripping leaves from trees, capture our interest by their unusual building endeavors. The adults are unattractive insects. Females are wingless, legless and worm-like. Males have transparent wings as a result of loss of their scales soon after emerging from their larval home. The larvae, however, are industrious home builders, constructing a portable shelter or bag which they live in all their lives. The EVERGREEN BAGWORM MOTH is a species found chiefly on red cedar and arbor vitae; at times entire trees may be covered with the pendant bags. Newly hatched larvae, in spring, assume a strange posture, walking on their "hands" with abdomens erect while weaving a silken band around their bodies, attaching to it bits of cedar foliage. By adding new material to the lower edge of the strange garment, a cylindrical case is formed which grows upward and soon passes the tip of the abdomen. Then it becomes cone-shaped and forms a bag enclosing all of the larva but its head. Now the larva returns to its normal position and moves about, dragging its bag-like home along with it.

At intervals the larva retreats within the sac, seals up the opening, molts, and pushes the cast-off skin through an opening left at the tip of the sac. When full grown the larva with its mobile home manages to migrate to another evergreen tree where there are fresh pastures, and attaches its bag to a twig. The time has come for the last stages of metamorphosis. Within the bag the larva becomes a pupa and, late in summer, an adult moth. The males emerge from their homes and spend a few days in carefree flight, but the wingless females have to remain in their larval homes, where mating takes place and eggs are laid. This duty done, the females die. Empty bags found on cedars and arbor vitae in winter were once the homes of males; bags filled with tiny yellow eggs were the homes of females. The eggs live through the winter, then hatch in spring into larvae which repeat the process.

The CODLING MOTH belongs to a family of small, night-flying, brownish or gray moths with mottled wings. The forewings are square-tipped, the hindwings have a fringe of hairs at their base. The Codling Moth, like many other insect pests, came uninvited from Europe over a century ago. In recent years it has cost the taxpayers several million dollars a year to control it. The Codling Moth has been called one of the world's most destructive insects. The larva, known as the Appleworm, hibernates in a cocoon on the bark of apple trees, and metamorphosis is so well timed that the adult emerges just as the first apple blossoms appear. They immediately lay flattened transparent eggs on the apple leaves, which hatch into dirty-white or pinkish caterpillars that crawl into the ripening fruit while it is still small. Pears and English walnuts are also attacked. The Codling Moth has now invaded every spot in the United States where apples are grown. A cousin of this moth, the MEXICAN JUMPING BEAN MOTH, has larvae which live in the seeds of a tropical shrub of the spurge family. When the wriggling larva throws itself around within the seed, it causes the mysterious actions of the bean.

The family of moths to which the TENT CATER-PILLAR belongs includes moths of medium size with gray or brownish yellow wings, often cross-striped in white. The moths appear in midsummer, laying egg masses covered with a brown foamy crust on the twigs of cherry trees. The eggs hatch the next spring, when the community-minded larvae set to work to construct the silken tents which disfigure so many of our trees. The black hairy larvae, striped with yellow, feed during the day on leaves near the shelter, then withdraw to the tent at night. Thus the best time to destroy these cater-

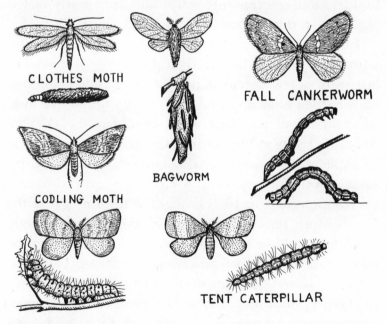

CLOTHES MOTH

FALL CANKERWORM

BAGWORM

CODLING MOTH

TENT CATERPILLAR

Many moths have notorious larvae which feed on our clothing and fabrics, destroy foliage of trees and garden plants, and bore into our fruits and vegetables.

– 147 –

pillars is at night when they are all congregated within their "tents."

The larvae known as MEASURING WORMS, or INCHWORMS, belong to a family of moths with slender bodies and broad wings, yellowish or reddish and often marked by wavy lines. In some species the females are wingless, as in the Cankerworms which attack elms and various fruit trees. The larvae have no legs on their middle abdominal segments, so have to move along by arching their bodies and bringing the hind quarters forward to the spot where the front legs stand, in a similar fashion to the cabbage loopers. Some of the larvae have the interesting habit of standing erect on their hindlegs and freezing into a stiff and apparently lifeless position. In this posture they look like small twigs.

Tussock moths are white or gray, medium-sized moths with hairy larvae which feed on the foliage of trees. The larvae of a few species have poison glands connected with barbed hairs and thus can cause a nettle-like rash. Most infamous member of the family is the GYPSY MOTH. Its introduction into this country is a typical example of the unintentional beginnings of an expensive invasion by a foreign insect. A French scientist who came to Massachusetts in 1869 brought with him eggs of the Gypsy Moth, hoping to cross it with the Silkworm Moth. One day while he was absent, his housekeeper did too thorough a cleaning job and swept out the eggs and caterpillars. In spite of immediate attempts to eradicate it, the Gypsy Moth moved rapidly through New England, leaving havoc in its wake among both forest and cultivated trees. The brown and black male Gypsy Moths are strong fliers, and can cover great distances in their search for the white and black females. During late summer the females lay some 400 eggs in clusters, covered with brownish hairs, which live through the winter. Hatching in May, the larvae feed for six weeks on foliage, then become pupae and emerge as adults in late summer when a new generation is started. Spread of the Gypsy Moth outside New England and New York is controlled by rigid plant quarantine laws. In the afflicted area no trees are immune from attack by this moth whose energetic caterpillars can strip a tree entirely bare of leaves, often causing its death.

This excursion into the lives of moths completes our introduction to the Lepidoptera. Few other groups of insects present such a variety of individuals, differing in attire and in personality. It is true that some of the species have eating habits so destructive that we have to wage constant warfare to keep them under control. But we should remember that this condition has been brought about by man's upsetting the delicate balance in nature whereby every species is ordinarily kept in check by biological conditions which even man can not alter with impunity.

Head-on view of a tiger moth

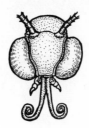

This terrifying creature is a greatly magnified housefly, photographed from a model in the American Museum of Natural History.

CHAPTER EIGHT

FLIES, DRAGONFLIES, AND CADDISFLIES

The word "fly," like "bug," is commonly used for many different kinds of small flying insects. But to an entomologist a fly is a special kind of insect belonging to the order *Diptera,* and characterized by a single pair of wings. These are the forewings; in place of the hindwings is a pair of knobbed balancing organs on short stalks. All other "flies" in popular language lack these features. We have already discovered that fireflies are beetles. Dragonflies, mayflies, caddisflies, and dobsonflies each belong to different groups of insects. First let us meet those in our insect parade which are true flies, and then become acquainted with a few which go by the name of fly in the popular sense.

True Flies

For centuries flies have been a threat to human health; they can well be called Public Enemy Number One of the insect world. Flies have been responsible for more human deaths than any other insect. They have achieved this unenviable distinction because of two traits. The mouth parts of some flies are specialized for piercing and sucking; flies with such weapons transmit many diseases including malaria and yellow fever. Other flies have sucking and lapping mouth parts; these carry micro-organisms on their bodies and legs, which cause typhoid fever, dysentery, cholera, and anthrax. The most thrilling chapters in the story of man's conquest of disease are those which tell of the discovery that insects carry disease and the methods by which such diseases can be eliminated. The picture is not entirely a gloomy one, however. Other kinds of flies are allies of man in killing harmful insects, and one group is second in importance only to bees in pollinating flowers and thus aiding production of fruit crops.

The head of a fly is mostly two huge compound eyes; in some species these take up so much space that when seen from in front the eyes touch each other. The mouth parts of a fly form a beak or proboscis, of which the lower lip is an important adjunct. In the house fly, this lip is expanded at the tip to form two broad sucking lobes. The body of the fly is more fragile than that of the other insects we have met, and its thin cuticle is bristly with hairs. Many species are so small as to be almost invisible; the tiny punkies and biting midges are well named "no-see-ums." There is one species of fly only a millimeter in length. Flies are for the most part dull-colored insects, lacking the sparkle and brilliance of many beetles and bugs.

The feeding habits of flies are varied. Some subsist on

the blood of birds, mammals, and man. Others are plant-feeders and so are injurious to crops. Still others are scavengers, feeding on dead and decaying animal remains. Such scavengers perform a very valuable service, for they are nature's street-cleaners and garbage-collectors. A carcass teeming with white maggots may not be a pretty sight, but it is nature's way of efficiently disposing of dead animals.

True flies undergo a complete metamorphosis. The eggs, usually laid in manure or in stagnant water, hatch into worm-like larvae known as maggots. Larvae that develop in the water, as those of mosquitoes, are called wigglers. After a hearty feeding period each larva becomes a pupa, which develops into the winged adult.

The HOUSE FLY hardly needs description. It does not bite but is nevertheless a dangerous disease carrier because it thrives in filth and refuse. From such places it carries disease germs on its mouth parts and legs. House flies are most numerous during the warm summer months; in the colder portions of the United States they practically disappear in winter. A house fly lays eggs every two weeks—perhaps twenty batches a season. This phenomenal rate of multiplication makes house flies a foe of no mean consequence. The invention of the automobile lessened the fly menace in an unexpected way by eliminating the horse from our highways, and with it most of the dung in which flies lay their eggs.

BLOW FLIES are small flies, much like house flies except for their metallic blue or green colors. These insects are sometimes called Bluebottle Flies and Greenbottle Flies. They are scavengers, eating and laying their eggs in decaying flesh. Some invade living tissues and lay their eggs in the open wounds of animals; as a result they are dangerous to cattle and domesticated animals. The Screw-worm is such a pest of livestock.

FRUIT FLIES are large-headed flies with green eyes, brown-black wings and orange, brown, or black bodies. Female fruit flies lay their eggs in plant tissues; when the larvae hatch they feed on the plant material thus conveniently at hand. A common fruit fly is the Apple Maggot, which many of us have unexpectedly found inside an otherwise attractive apple. Two species of fruit fly have been a threat to orange and grapefruit growers: the Mexican Fruit Fly and the Mediterranean Fruit Fly. The story of man's battle with the Mediterranean Fruit Fly in Florida has a happy ending, for such prompt and effective measures were taken that today this injurious species has been eradicated from the state. Another group of fruit flies known as vinegar flies includes *Drosophila*—a name well known to biologists. Because of its rapid reproductive rate and the ease with which it

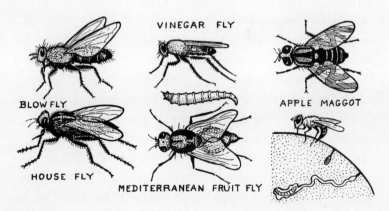

True flies, such as these common representatives, have only one pair of wings, and larvae usually known as maggots.

can be raised under laboratory conditions, this fly has become to genetics what white mice have been to medical research. Much of our knowledge of heredity has come from studies on this insect.

FLOWER FLIES like to feast on nectar. Thus they are well named, for they can always be found around flowers where they perform a useful service as pollinators. They are colorful insects, often marked with yellow and white. Some species look much like bees and wasps for which they are often mistaken, but the single pair of wings reveals their real identity. Flower flies do not bite or sting. Their larvae are valuable by keeping in check the numbers of aphids and mealybugs.

The most painful experience one can have with flies is to be the victim of a hungry, determined HORSE FLY. These large flies, some almost an inch in length, are strong fliers. Being numerous around water, they are a nuisance at the seashore. Those with bright green eyes

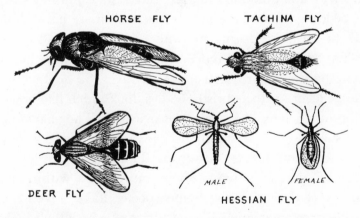

Female biting flies (Deer Fly, Horse Fly) feed on blood; other flies (Hessian Fly) destroy our crops; but some flies (Tachina Fly) indirectly aid man by laying their eggs in other, injurious insects.

are known as Green-headed Flies; those with spotted wings are Deer Flies. Male horse flies are harmless insects, content with spending their days buzzing from flower to flower, feeding on nectar and honey. It is the female which demands blood, and gets it by biting and sucking warm-blooded animals, including man. If you look a horse fly in the face, you can see the difference between a male and female; in the male the eyes meet in the middle of the face, while in the female the eyes are separated from each other.

GALL MIDGES are tiny hump-backed flies with long legs and peculiar banded antennae. Most species are less than a quarter of an inch in length. These insects cause galls on leaves, and also destroy crops. The Hessian Fly lays its eggs in the stems of wheat. As the larvae develop they suck the sap and destroy wheat stem tissue; the plant dies, or is so weakened that a slight wind will blow it down. During the Revolutionary War this fly came unbidden to the United States, in hay used as bedding by the Hessians. It has done more harm than all the Hessians during the war.

TACHINA FLIES redeem, to some extent, the harm done by their more destructive relatives. Some Tachina flies, except for their bristly bodies, look much like house flies; others look like small bees or wasps. They have the unusual habit of laying their eggs in the bodies of many insects which destroy our crops. The larvae develop as internal parasites, living their entire lives within the bodies of their victims. Some species have solved the problem of breathing while within the body of their host, in a unique way, by hooking-up with the tracheae and utilizing the host's respiratory system. Tachina flies are common parasites of caterpillars, consuming the entire body from within, leaving only a hollow shell and a few fragments of skin. Some species of Tachina Fly were brought over from Europe to New England to keep in check the gypsy and browntail moths; they are also used in the battle against Japanese Beetles.

MOSQUITOES, like House Flies, scarcely need description. These delicate-bodied and long-legged insects have a particularly deadly proboscis, capable of piercing flesh like a hypodermic needle. Male mosquitoes mind their own business, frequenting flowers where they feed on nectar and other plant liquids. It is the female mosquito which bites man. The female must feed on blood before the eggs can develop properly; driven by this instinctive knowledge, she has become a nuisance to everyone who enjoys the outdoors. This sex also has the ability to vibrate thin chitinous structures covering the spiracles of the thorax; the resulting high-pitched song may be pleasant to a mosquito, but it is often as irritating to us as the actual bite. The sexes can be recognized by the antennae; those of the male are much more feathery and plume-like than those of the female.

Mosquitoes lay their eggs in stagnant water. If laid on soil they require some water, even if only a tiny puddle, in which to hatch. The larvae, or wigglers, have chewing mouth parts and feed on microscopic plant and animal life. Many species breathe by means of a "snorkel" tube at the tip of the abdomen; the wigglers make frequent trips to the surface in getting air by its use. This habit makes it easy to exterminate mosquito breeding sites by covering the water with oil or some other liquid through which the "snorkel" cannot penetrate. Being unable then to get to the air, the larvae suffocate. Mosquito pupae, unlike most pupae, are active and also come to the surface to breathe; they are known as "tumblers." Adult mosquitoes spend the daylight hours hiding in the shade, or under logs and leaves; they are most common, as all hikers know, in damp and dimly lighted wooded hollows. The common Salt Marsh Mosquito is a well known seashore pest of the New Jersey lowlands and surrounding areas. Other mosquitoes have adapted themselves to a wide climatic range, being numerous even in the Arctic where they survive winter as eggs or adults, or even as larvae, frozen in the ice.

Caddisflies

CADDISFLIES are medium-sized insects with two pairs of inconspicuously colored membranous and hairy wings,

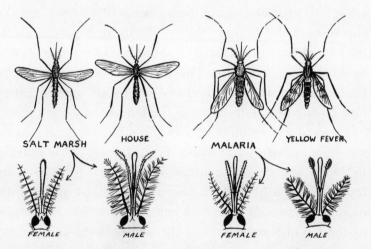

SALT MARSH   HOUSE   MALARIA   YELLOW FEVER

FEMALE   MALE   FEMALE   MALE

Some mosquitoes (Salt-marsh and House) are merely a source of annoyance, but others (Malaria and Yellow Fever) transmit diseases. The male usually has more feathery and plume-like antennae than the female.

usually held roof-like over the body when not in use. Caddisflies can easily be mistaken for moths, but their antennae are long and slender; they are poor fliers, walking about by preference on their long legs. Adults are common by day around streams and ponds, but at night collect at lights. Since their chewing mouth parts include much reduced mandibles, caddisflies live chiefly on a liquid diet.

Caddisfly eggs are laid in the water, in strings or masses. The larvae of some species can be found in the flowing water of small streams; other species prefer the more quiet water of swamps and ponds. Caddisfly larvae look like caterpillars, but the abdomen bears thread-like gills and, at its tip, a pair of hooked appendages. They

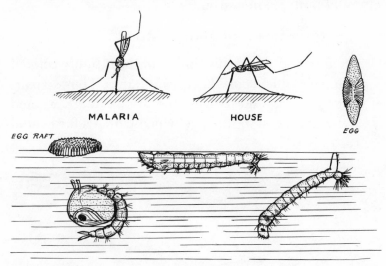

MALARIA   HOUSE   EGG

EGG RAFT

Malaria and House Mosquitoes have different habits of holding their bodies when biting; their larvae also differ, those of the House Mosquito hanging at an angle from the surface of the water, those of the Malaria Mosquito floating parallel to the surface. The pupae are also aquatic.

– 159 –

are omnivorous feeders with any kind of small aquatic animal or plant on the menu. Caddisfly larvae are unusual in being builders of portable homes. Sand, bits of gravel, twigs, parts of leaves are collected and cemented together by a silk produced in special glands opening into the mouth. The resulting structure is an elongated case which serves as a portable home in which the larva spends most of its life; with head projecting from the case, it lies alert for bits of food which drift by. Caddisflies and their peculiar cases can be found on the underside of stones in streams. Some species go a step further in their engineering and construct cup-shaped nets to collect food, with the open portion facing upstream. The caddisfly makes daily trips from its nearby case to these specially built feeding grounds.

Dragonflies and Damselflies

Dragonflies and damselflies are trim, beautifully colored flying insects which look like tiny airplanes. The two pairs of wings are long and narrow; the thorax and elongated abdomen form a slim fuselage which extends far behind

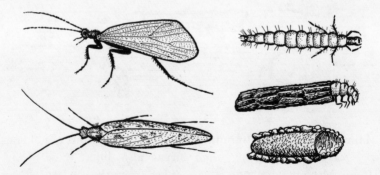

Caddisfly larvae are aquatic, and build peculiar cases in which to live, made of sand, twigs and bits of debris cemented together.

the wings. The cellophane-like wings are pigmented in spots with brilliant black, blue, brown, and red; the thorax and abdomen is often bright blue or green. Large compound eyes which make up most of the head enable these adept fliers to locate the tiny midges and mosquitoes which make up much of their diet. Adults spend most of the time on the wing. The legs, rarely used for walking, serve chiefly as a basket in which flying insects are scooped up by the dragonflies as they dart about in the air. Dragonflies do not bite or sting; they are entirely harmless in spite of folk-tales that they sew up one's ears. Being insect eaters, they perform a service to man in destroying many injurious species.

Dragonflies are heavy-bodied insects which are strong fliers; they hold their wings outstretched when at rest. Damselflies on the other hand have slimmer bodies and are weak fliers, resting often and holding their wings together over the back. Dragonflies lay their eggs on the surface of the water or on water plants, while damselflies more usually place theirs in the tissues of aquatic plants. Both undergo a simple metamorphosis with the nymphs

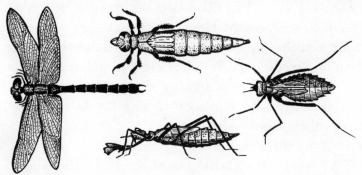

Dragonfly nymphs are aquatic, and are common objects along stream beds; their gills are internal.

molting as they become larger. When metamorphosis is completed, the nymph crawls out of the water, splits its larval skin along the back, and crawls out as a winged adult. These cast-off skins are often seen on logs and twigs near water.

Dragonfly nymphs are completely aquatic, feeding on small aquatic insects, on occasional tadpoles or small fish. They have a surprising ability suddenly to dart forward, as if jet-propelled. Actually they do have a type of jet propulsion. Dragonfly nymphs have a peculiar type of gill-breathing, with the gills located in the terminal part of their alimentary canal. Breathing consists of taking in water through the anus and forcing it out again through the same opening. When a dragonfly nymph is excited and wants to get away in a hurry, the rapidly increased breathing expels water from the anus with such force that it propels the insect forward. The gills of damselfly nymphs are leaf-like structures at the end of the abdomen. These nymphs swing their body from side to side as fish do, and the gills serve the same purpose in locomotion as the fish's tail.

DARNING NEEDLES are big dragonflies, about three inches in length. These are the familiar dragonflies with green thorax, blue abdomen, and gauze-like wings. Darning Needles are found around ponds and streams. The TEN SPOT is a smaller dragonfly with a dull-colored body and wings spotted with brown. Ten Spots are fast fliers which skim close to the surface of the water in scooping up their insect prey.

NARROW-WINGED DAMSELFLIES are larger, reaching a length of two inches; their wings narrow gradually at the base. They are usually found only near streams. In these insects the males and females are colored differently. The male RUBY SPOT, for example, has a red spot at the base of the wing which the female lacks. Similarly in the Black-winged Damselfly, the wings of the male are black, but those of the female are dark gray with a white spot on the edge of each wing.

We are apt to think of animals in terms of whether they are useful or harmful because their way of life conflicts with ours. But from the viewpoint of the insect, their habits are the means by which they survive to carry on their own race; to them, man is only another aspect of their environment. When considered in this way even the flies are interesting. It is true that we consider some of them—house flies, mosquitoes, midges, and gnats—disreputable members of the animal world. But even so their adaptations command our admiration. In addition many of the "flies" in the popular sense—the dragonflies, damselflies, caddisflies, and others—contribute original body designs and colors to enliven the insect parade.

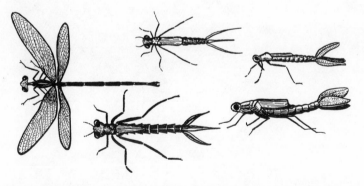

Damselfly nymphs are aquatic, breathing by visible gills in the form of three leaf-like projections from the rear of the abdomen.

A Bumblebee poises in mid-air as it readies itself to gather honey from the blossoms of a lily-of-the-valley.

CHAPTER NINE

THE SOCIAL INSECTS

We have met many different kinds of grasshoppers, bugs, beetles, flies, butterflies and moths in our insect parade. These have revealed an astonishing variety of body adaptations designed to aid them in getting food, in moving about by legs or by wings, in defending themselves from their enemies, and—in the case of carnivorous species—in catching their prey. They have also shown great ingenuity in guaranteeing the successful development of their eggs and larvae. As individuals these insects command our admiration even if at times their superior fitness for survival becomes a nuisance in our outdoor activities and a threat to our agriculture.

In most species each insect is entirely on its own, and has to rely upon its inherited physique and prowess if it is to complete its life span. Yet two groups of insects have tried and accepted cooperative living. Man feels he is unique in his belief that the cooperation of individuals will attain the greatest good for all. But millions of years before man tried this way of life, certain insect groups solved the problem of survival by a highly developed social organization. These two insect groups are the *Isoptera,* or termites, and the *Hymenoptera,* or wasps, bees, and ants. These insects exhibit individual adaptations as ingenious as those of other insects, and in addition have developed a division of labor resulting in different types, or castes, of individuals. Their insect community has often been compared with that of human society. But the insects have gone far beyond man in many ways which, although guaranteeing the survival of the group as a whole, reduces the individual to an automatic machine. The insect community differs from ours in another important respect: its guiding force is blind instinct rather than intelligence.

The *Hymenoptera* have two pairs of thin membranous wings, the smaller hindwing in many cases held to the forewing by tiny hooks on its margin. Ants are an exception to the generally winged character of the order, since the worker ant—which is the ant ordinarily encountered—is wingless. Metamorphosis is complete, the egg becoming an adult through larva and pupa stages. The biting parts of the adult are modified for various purposes. Those of the bees form a long tongue for sucking nectar from the throat of flowers. Those of the wasps are capable of macerating and dismembering other insects. Ants have mandibles strong enough to crack open seeds. The first segment of the abdomen of the ant is joined to the last segment of the thorax, but the second segment is so constricted that the insect seems to have a waist. In this order we find the only insects with true stingers, which are, as we have seen, the ovipositors of the females. Since males lack this egg-laying tool, they are unable to sting.

Members of this order are among the most beneficial insects. The bees, and some wasps, fly from flower to flower in search of nectar and in so doing transfer pollen from stamen to pistil. Unless this pollen transfer takes place, flowers do not produce fruit and seed. Thus the pollination of our fruit trees and crop plants is a service of incalculable worth to the farmer. Bees also furnish us with the oldest of sweetening materials, honey. Many wasps feed on insects and thus are our allies in reducing the numbers of agricultural pests. Ants are of little economic importance except in loosening soil, occasionally becoming household pests.

The *Isoptera,* or termites, are also known as white ants, an unfortunate common name since they are not ants and are often not white. They feed on wood—either as trees, logs, or roots—and on structures made of wood. Their destruction of supporting timbers of houses, floors, and furniture has been well publicized. The few American species cause an annual loss of $40,000,000. Fortunately for us most species of termites are tropical. Winged and wingless individuals occur in the termite colony, as among the ants. Since any kind of winged ant seen around your home may make you worry for fear it is a termite, reference to the table on the following page may reassure you by helping to identify these insects.

Wasps

Most of us undoubtedly think of wasps and hornets in terms of an unfortunate experience in being stung by

How to Tell a Termite from an Ant	
Termite	*Ant*
has a soft body	has a hard body
has abdomen and thorax broadly joined together	has abdomen and thorax separated by a waist
both pairs of wings are the same size	hindwings are smaller than forewings
wings at rest held flat against body	wings at rest held above the body
wingless forms are light-colored	wingless forms are dark-colored or black

their sharp ovipositor, which they seem ready to use without provocation. However this group of insects reveals a number of clever adaptations for their special way of life, and activities much more ingenious than any we have already encountered. Wasps include both solitary and social species. Gall wasps, digger wasps, and potter wasps are some of the solitary members of the family. The social wasps are the familiar hornets which build large papery homes as aerial apartment houses in which a thousand or more individuals may live.

GALL WASPS are small brownish insects with a thorax and an abdomen which appear circular when seen from the side; the head is underslung beneath the thorax. The female wasp has a long, coiled ovipositor with which she can puncture plants and deposit her eggs in the tissues of the leaves and stems. Oaks, roses, and plants in the sunflower family are frequently selected by gall wasps as sites for their eggs. As the larvae develop, substances are produced which cause abnormal growth of the plant, resulting in the spherical galls, especially common on oak leaves. Galls have been used as a source of tannic acid, coloring for inks, and dyes.

A number of different kinds of wasps are known as digger wasps because of their habit of digging homes in the earth. The CICADA KILLER is a giant in this group, with a black and yellow striped abdomen; fortunately it shows its ferocity only against cicadas. Most of the time the adults fly peaceably from flower to flower, sipping nectar, or feasting on the sap oozing out of the bark of a tree. Males spend all their lives feeding in this way. But when a female becomes mature, as a

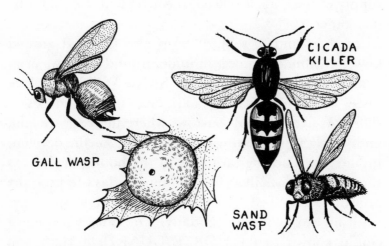

Female Gall Wasps puncture and lay their eggs in plants; as the larva develops they stimulate the stems and leaves to abnormal growth resulting in the gall. The Cicada Killer is a large wasp with yellow and black abdomen. Sand Wasps live in burrows which are kept well stocked with flies as food.

prospective mother she becomes a murderous demon, searching out cicadas on the ground, among the trees, and even pursuing them in the air. Diving at the more clumsy cicada, the wasp aims a well directed thrust with her stinger, and the cicada tumbles to earth. The venom includes an anesthetic which paralyzes the cicada. Although the wasp is smaller than its victim, it manages to drag the body to the entrance of its burrow. The wasp will even climb a tree with its load, clasping the cicada beneath its thorax, and glide off to its nest in the ground. The burrow ends in a nursery room, where the unconscious cicada is stowed away. The wasp carefully lays an egg on the body—always under one of the middle legs—and then seals up the cell with earth. After three days the egg hatches into a larva which grows fat on the supply of fresh meat placed so conveniently at hand by its mother.

Another kind of solitary wasp also is found around flowers; it builds its nest in underground burrows or in homes constructed of mud. The SAND WASP is a black insect with greenish white markings, often found at seashores. It lives in small burrows where the eggs are laid, and which are stocked with flies as food for the developing larvae. The eggs are laid on the bodies of flies, as those of Cicada Killers are laid on cicadas. To keep the growing larva well fed, the mother sand wasp brings fresh flies to her offspring daily. The sand wasp has a cousin known as the HORSE GUARD, a black and yellow wasp whose favorite hunting ground for flies is around horses.

POTTER WASPS are solitary wasps with an artistic bent. They fashion symmetrical little urns of sand or clay, with a broad lip around the mouth. After completing her potter's task, the female wasp stocks the cozy nest with paralyzed caterpillars, and suspends an egg by a slender thread above the cache of food. The chilled larva lies motionless all winter, but when warm days of spring arrive it resumes its growth and changes into a pupa. Later as a wasp, it bites its way out of the side of the urn.

MUD-DAUBERS are solitary wasps with a liking for doing masonry work. They fashion their tan or brown mud nests on walls and under protecting eaves, with the openings pointed downward. When a number of these nests are plastered side by side they look like small organ pipes. One kind of Mud-dauber Wasp is brownish with a yellow-spotted body and yellow legs. Another is metallic blue, with blue wings. A northern species provisions its nest with spiders; a southern species uses roaches for this purpose.

YELLOW JACKETS are social wasps that often build their nests in the ground, exactly where a young

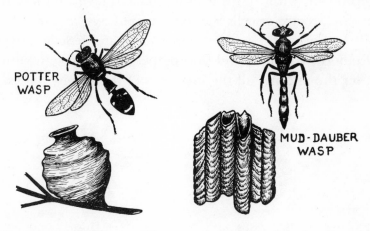

POTTER WASP

MUD-DAUBER WASP

Potter and Mud-dauber Wasps are the masons of the insect world.

naturalist is likely to step on it. They also have homes in tree stumps and under rotting logs, or under the eaves of houses. Adults catch insects and chew them to a pulp, then feed it to the larvae. Larger in size, and colored black and white, are the BALD-FACED HORNETS; these are the wasps which construct the large spherical nests which hang from limbs of trees or nestle under the eaves. Nests two feet long are common, with several hundred tenants. The nest is made of a papery material, chewed from woody fibers by the wasps and fashioned into a waterproof outer wall for the pendant apartment house. Such a nest is begun by a single female who survived the winter by hibernating in a crevice in the bark of a tree, or in a crack in a stonewall. She begins the nest with a single small hanging room, in which she lays her first eggs. She tends to feeding the larvae until a brood has hatched into workers who can assist in constructing additions to the nest and in securing food for future young. New rooms and floors are built, from the top down, with ramps leading to each level; hundreds of small rooms or cells lead off the hallways, and in each she lays an egg. Late in summer male and female wasps are born who mate and thus perpetuate the colony. But after the mating, all the members of the colony die ex-

Familiar social wasps are the Bald-faced Hornet and Yellow Jacket.

cept a few fertile females, and the hornets' nest becomes deserted. It will never be occupied again, for the few prospective mothers who survive the winter will construct new nests the following spring.

Bees

Bees differ from wasps in many ways. Bees have stout hairy bodies, wasps are streamlined and without hairs on thorax and abdomen. Bees are herbivorous, relying on pollen and nectar not only for their own sustenance but for nourishment of their young, while most wasps are carnivorous or live as parasites on other insects. The legs of bees are modified for transporting pollen, which is collected on the hairy thorax and abdomen, and removed by the forelegs and middle legs to a pollen basket on the hindleg. The foreleg has a comb-like slit between two of its segments which is used for cleaning the antennae when they become covered with sticky pollen. Sharp

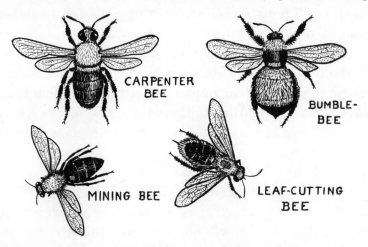

Most bees have stout hairy bodies which are a contrast to the sleeker bodies of the wasps.

claws and adhesive pads on the feet enable bees to climb rough surfaces and cling to smooth ones. Greatest difference between bees and wasps is that the bees have learned thrift, collecting and storing food (honey) on which they can live through the winter. For this reason bee colonies can be permanent, lasting from year to year, while wasps form new colonies each year.

Most species of bees lead solitary lives, after the fashion of wasps. Many of these are valuable wild bees which pollinate our crops. Their numbers have decreased however because the spread of civilization has eliminated many of their home sites in the soil. One group of these solitary bees is the MINING BEES, of which the Alkali Bee is a representative. This bee lives west of the Rocky Mountains, building its underground nests in the salty soils of areas with scanty vegetation. Although each bee leads its own life, they make burrows next to each other; at times thousands of nests can be found on an acre of land. Each female digs her own nest, and in it makes about a dozen little nursery rooms, each to be occupied by an egg. The egg is laid on a ball of pollen and nectar, carefully prepared beforehand by the mother. The first larvae to complete the pupa stage emerge and join their parents in pollinating alfalfa plants. The others spend the winter as larvae and complete their metamorphosis the following spring. Alfalfa fields planted near nesting sites of these bees give unusually high yields of alfalfa.

Another solitary bee is the LEAF-CUTTING BEE, a large hairy bee which may be black, blue, green, or purple; they are the pollinators of our cultivated clovers. Leaf-cutting Bees make their burrows in the ground or in hollow trees, lining the rooms with bits of leaves. These bees are the culprits which leave neatly cut circular and oval holes in leaves, especially those of rose bushes. The bees carry the pieces of leaves to the burrows, using the circular sections for cell partitions, the oval ones as wallpaper for the hallways. A typical nest consists of ten or twelve nursery rooms, each with a small pile of pollen and nectar and each the birthplace of a tiny larva.

CARPENTER BEES are solitary bees with a wood-boring habit. A small species, blue-green in color, excavates its nests in the pithy stems of raspberry and blackberry bushes. A large species looks much like a Honey Bee in size and coloring, but the top of its abdomen is smooth rather than hairy. The wood-boring instinct sometimes makes this bee a nuisance to homeowners; a Carpenter Bee can drill a quarter-inch hole with the precision of an auger, through the hardest of wood exteriors. These holes terminate in the cells where the eggs are laid and provisions stored for the developing larvae.

Social bees belong to the Honey Bee family. In the United States this includes the native Bumblebee as well as the introduced Honey Bee. The BUMBLEBEE, our largest bee, is most abundant in the central states; it has a black body with brilliant yellow, orange, or red markings. Our Bumblebees construct new homes every year in old mouse burrows, rotting logs, and stumps. Three kinds of individuals live in a colony of Bumblebees: fertile females capable of laying eggs, or *queens;* females usually without reproductive powers, or *workers;* and males, or *drones.* The colony has its beginning in a young queen who alone has survived the winter by hibernating in a protected spot. After selecting a site, she usually redecorates and renovates the interior, using grass and moss to make it livable. When complete the nest is a spherical room with a small entrance hole. The queen makes many trips to the first spring flowers for pollen and nectar, which she molds into a small mound in the middle of the floor of the nest. On top of this she builds a circular cell of wax, secreted by her own body, and in it she lays seven to sixteen eggs. As a final preparation for raising a family, she places food supply in the form of a honeypot in a handy spot inside the entrance of the nest.

The succeeding behavior is most unusual for an insect. Mounting the pile of eggs, the queen proceeds to incubate them with her body warmth, as if she were a setting hen. In the four days it takes the eggs to hatch, she eats from her honeypot or makes quick trips to the fields. The young larvae find a ready-made food in the pollen paste

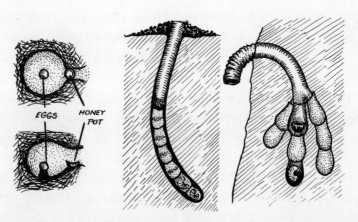

Many bees nest in the ground; such are the Bumblebee (*left*) and the wild bees with tunnels in the ground (*center*) or in the sides of cliffs (*right*).

bedding on which they were born. As this supply diminishes, the mother bee brings in fresh food, injecting it into the pollen paste which the larvae eat while small, later feeding the food to the larvae by mouth. In a few weeks the larvae are full grown, and wrap themselves in a papery cocoon in which they will become pupae. The attentive queen again mounts the pile of youngsters, incubating the cocoons as she did the eggs. If the weather is chilly, she warms them by rhythmic contractions of her abdomen.

The first brood, all females, is made up of individuals much smaller than their mother. They are born to be workers, and lose no time in taking over the duties of collecting pollen and nectar, constructing new nursery mounds. The queen can now tend exclusively to laying eggs. When a new brood of larvae hatches, the workers assume the role of nursemaids. Since the colony grows in size by the addition of each new generation of workers, at the height of the season, a bumblebee colony may number 500 inhabitants. Later in the summer some workers lay eggs; these develop into drones. Certain worker larvae, because of being fed an especially rich diet, grow into "princesses"—females capable of becoming queens. During mating flight of drones and young queens, the future of the race is determined. For as winter approaches all the workers and drones perish, the nest becomes deserted. But a few of the fertile queens will hibernate and repeat the colony building next spring.

The HONEY BEE follows the same pattern as the Bumblebee in its social system, with three castes: queens, drones, and workers. But the Honey Bee community is a permanent establishment, continuing from year to year. This permanence has made possible such a complex and amazing organization that its activities and achievements is proof of the statement, "truth is stranger than fiction." The Honey Bee is not a native American, but was brought here by the first settlers. Indians called it the "White Man's Fly." Honey Bees have been a productive companion of man for over 4000 years, although they can hardly be called "domesticated," since man has not been able to change their nature or habits.

A Honey Bee colony is a busy city with a population which may run as high as 80,000 individuals. Each colony usually has only one *queen,* who can be recognized by her long abdomen, toothed mandibles, smooth retractable stinger, and legs lacking pollen baskets. Several hundred *drones* also live in the colony; these have chunky bodies, large eyes, and lack stingers. The royal family is outnumbered by the thousands of their laboring class, or *workers.* Workers are smaller females, normally incapable of laying eggs. Their bodies are very hairy, their legs bear tools of the pollen-collecting trade in the form of pollen baskets. The stinger of a worker is barbed and not retractable, which means that when this bee stings, the stinger is torn from the insect's body and left in the victim, causing the bee to die. Among their other accomplishments, bees have learned how to control the sex of their offspring. Drones, or males, are produced

(*See opposite page*) The Honey Bee has a society made up of queens, drones, and workers. The worker bee has legs marvelously adapted for the tasks to be performed in gathering pollen. At lower left is a magnified view of the bee's stinger; lower center, the bee's tongue; and lower right, the clawed foot.

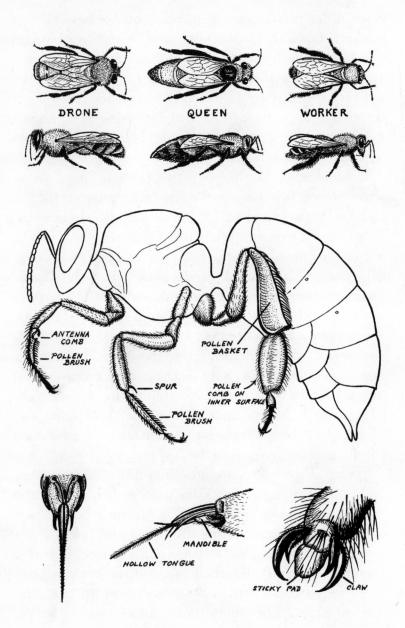

DRONE   QUEEN   WORKER

ANTENNA COMB

POLLEN BRUSH

SPUR

POLLEN BRUSH

POLLEN BASKET

POLLEN COMB ON INNER SURFACE

HOLLOW TONGUE

MANDIBLE

STICKY PAD   CLAW

from unfertilized eggs of queens, or occasionally, of workers. But only queens who have mated can lay eggs which become females. Thus the production of males and females in the bee population is determined by whether the eggs are fertilized or not. Since the work of the colony is performed by females (workers), periodic mating and the presence of drones is necessary to keep the colony in existence.

A beehive, during daylight hours in summer, hums with activity. Nowhere in the animal kingdom is there a comparable scene of such feverish yet orderly activity. From sunrise to sunset, a stream of workers passes in and out of the entrance to the bee city, making continuous trips to the flowers and bringing back pollen and nectar. Bees travel several miles for a load, and careful observers have recorded that some bees travel as far as eight miles. These field workers are bees who have already put in a few weeks' apprenticeship inside the hive. During their first days outside, they stay near the hive entrance and practice using their wings, reconnoitering to locate objects around the entrance so they can find their way back home. They also serve as defenders if an enemy tries to gain entrance into the hive.

Young field workers are attired in fluffy golden-yellow hair and gleaming wings. They work so strenuously and continuously however that in a month their bodies have darkened and become almost hairless and many wings are tattered. During the active summer period, a worker becomes decrepit and ready for retirement or death when only two months old. Workers born in late summer, who spend the winter doing indoor tasks instead of strenuously collecting honey and pollen, may live for six months. Field workers do not collect their pollen and nectar aimlessly, as butterflies seem to do; theirs is a one-track mind, concentrating on a particular kind of flower and visiting thoroughly every tiny blossom. As soon as their two pollen baskets are filled and their crop has a full load of nectar they fly back to the hive in a "bee-line," give up their burdens, and fly back to the same kind of flower for another load.

The dense coat of fluffy hairs on the worker's body becomes covered with pollen as it visits the flowers; this it brushes off with forelegs and middlelegs and packs into pellets, as large as its own head, in the two pollen baskets. The nectar sucked up by the long tongue of the worker is temporarily stored in the crop, where partial digestion begins, changing the cane sugar (sucrose) into invert sugar (levulose and dextrose). This is the beginning of the conversion of nectar into honey. On its return to the hive, the worker delivers its pellets of pollen to "warehousemen," workers who pack the pollen into special storage cells, tamping it in with their heads. The honey is stored separately in other cells, where it is further processed by "chemists" into refined honey. Bees have an instinctive knowledge about balanced diets for their young. The pollen furnishes the fats and the tissue-building proteins for the growing larvae, the nectar contributes the carbohydrates for energy. Adults can live on nectar alone, but young bees need both kinds of food. The pollen pellets are often called "bee bread."

If we could enter the hive, we would find very congested living quarters. The basis of the hive is a hanging comb, made of hexagonal cells, closely packed in vertical rows of two placed back to back. Between them the passageways are just large enough for the bees to get from cell to cell. Parallel rows of combs add living and storage quarters. Small cells, about one-fifth of an inch in diameter serve as nurseries for worker larvae and as pollen-storage rooms. Larger cells, about a quarter of an inch in diameter, provide nurseries for drones and bins for honey. Special large cells are reserved for royal suites, in which future queens are born.

These passageways teem with adult bees, each with its special job. Busy as the life of a field worker may seem, the workers inside the hive are part of an even busier activity. Whether a worker is to do field work or inside work depends upon its age. During spring and summer, young workers remain within the hive for the first few weeks of their lives; then they graduate to the outside world, go through a short period of flight training, and spend the rest of their lives as field workers. The young workers who do the household chores are specialists in various duties. Some are housemaids, others are nurse-maids; some are carpenters and repairmen, others ware-housemen and industrial chemists. There are some which function even as heating and air-conditioning engineers! The housemaids keep the passageways clean and sanitary. They also have the responsibility of cleaning and polishing each cell before an egg is placed in it. Since the queen may lay 1500 eggs a day, this means plenty of work for the housemaids.

Numerous workers are kept busy as nursemaids. Bee babies are helpless, blind, and limbless, tucked in cells with little room to move about. Sticking their tiny heads out of the cells, they are constantly calling, in bee language, for food. Nursemaids scurry back and forth between the storage bins of honey and pollen and the demanding babies, keeping their hungry mouths filled. This is quite a task, for the appetite of a bee larva is tremendous; they eat so much that in the six-day period of their lives they increase their weight 1500 times. In human terms this would mean that a baby weighing six pounds at birth would in less than a week weigh as much as an elephant. On the seventh day the larva stops eating; workers place a porous cap over the cell, and the larva spins a cocoon within which it will become transformed into a winged bee. Twenty-one days after the egg was laid, the young worker emerges to take its place in the community.

Building, repair work, and maintenance are the duties of other workers. The carpenters and mechanics build new combs and cells as the population of their city increases and new storage bins are needed for the ever-increasing flow of pollen and honey into the hive. A resinous material, gathered from the sticky buds of poplar trees, is used to mend cracks in the walls and combs, and to insulate and waterproof the outer walls of their community dwelling. The industrial chemists take over the flavoring, blending, and processing of the honey. As brought to the hive by the workers, the nectar contains an excess of water which would cause fermentation during storage. The honey is evaporated to a more concentrated solution by air currents, set up by continuous fanning of the workers' wings. In commercial hives as much as a quarter of the volume of nectar brought in during the day is lost nightly by forced evaporation.

Most incredible of all is the way in which workers function as heating and air-conditioning experts. They keep the nursery rooms and royal quarters cool in summer by fanning the air with their wings; a temperature in excess of 93 degrees retards egg-laying and growth of the larvae. As cool weather sets in, the workers keep the center of the brood chamber from dropping to dangerously low temperature. A loose cluster of workers surrounds this chamber and acts as an insulating layer, keeping the temperature at about 57 degrees. A more compact inner layer of workers move their wings and bodies enough to release heat, and thus keep the center of the hive comfortable. As the workers on the outer layer get cold, they move toward the center and are replaced by workers who have been nearer the center of the colony. Bees have no special soldier caste; theirs is a democratic social life where workers are drafted in time of danger. Each worker has to be ready to sacrifice its life in stinging an enemy; for after one sting, it dies.

The queen is not a royal personage in the sense that she rules the colony. Actually she is merely a highly mechanized mother, an automatic egg-laying machine which turns out hundreds of thousands of eggs in her lifetime of three to four years. In a protected brood chamber she begins at a slow rate of a few eggs a day, eventually steps up her production to 1800 a day at the height of the summer. The eggs are placed in shiny clean cells; fertilized eggs will become workers, unfertilized ones will grow into drones. During the first three days of their lives all the larvae are fed alike, with a jelly which is a milky secretion from the heads of worker nursemaids. After this period, most of the larvae are given a less rich diet, and as a result grow into sterile females, or workers. A few larvae are selected to be fed the royal jelly for the full five and a half days of larval development. These are predestined to become "princesses," capable of growing into the young queens who found new colonies.

Larvae which hatch into males make up a very small proportion of the colony. As drones they lead a carefree life for a short time. They do not have to work in the fields, nor do any of the manual labor indoors. Having no stinger, they are exempt from military duty. Unlike queens and workers, they are free to visit other hives, and are tolerated good-naturedly as long as summer lasts and there is plenty of food for all. But when cold weather sets in, the frugal workers eye their honey supply thriftily and drive the shiftless drones out into the

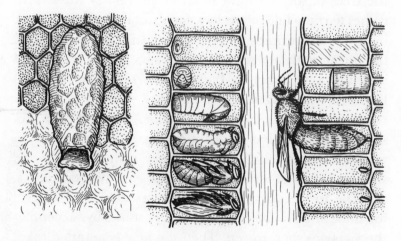

The queen bee is born in a special chamber (*left*) resembling a peanut; worker cells appear at the left of the queen's cell, male cells at the right. The queen (*right*) is kept busy laying eggs, one at the bottom of each cell; these develop through the stages seen in the cells behind the queen.

– 185 –

cold world, where they perish for lack of protection and food. Fathers are not highly respected members of the bee community. Their only service for the common good is during the swarming season, when they mate with young princesses on their nuptial flights. But even these drones die shortly after the honeymoon.

As summer progresses, the hive is bursting with more honey than can be used, every storage bin is full and the busy workers fill all available space. Then on some fine warm day, usually late in the morning, a restlessness comes over the colony. Hundreds of workers loaf around the entrance, and the throng grows. The buzzing becomes louder, and finally the old queen appears to join her workers. This is a signal for the restless bees to swarm, and they move slowly, like a hazy ball of smoke, through the trees to some distant field. Occasionally the swarm comes to rest while scouts look for a suitable nesting site. A hollow tree, perhaps an accessible attic, is selected, and the queen with her retinue of workers begins the task of building a new home. Back in the old hive, now relieved of its congestion, a princess emerges from her royal cell. With unladylike behavior, she at once makes sure of her position by eliminating all possible rivals, mutilating the cells in which other princesses may be slumbering. If other active princesses are found, there is a battle to the death; queen bees reserve their stingers for these sisterly duels. The workers stand by, accepting the victor as their queen. Then the new generation takes over the hive until another year when again the "reigning" queen mother departs with her swarm to form a new colony, relinquishing the old homestead to the younger group.

Ants

All ants are social insects and thus are more highly specialized than other members of the Hymenoptera. In contrast to the bees, ants are of little importance either as allies or enemies. Yet from ancient times until today ants have fascinated man. This insect has been observed and studied by hundreds of naturalists for no other reason than its highly developed social system, its unusual occupations, and unique relationships with other insects.

Ants are small insects which may be black, brown, yellow, or red. Their mouth parts are adapted for biting and sucking, and some individuals have stingers. The antennae of ants are bent in such a peculiar way that they appear to have "elbows." Ants have conspicuously narrow "waists" as a result of the constriction of one of the abdominal segments. Most ants are fond of sweets, and for this reason become pests in kitchens and storerooms; they carry no diseases, and lack the filthy habits of flies. Ants, unlike their relatives the bees and wasps, are terrestrial animals, living on and under the ground where they build galleries and living quarters and storerooms. Some expand their homes above ground in piles of dirt, pine needles, and woodland litter to form the familiar anthills. Ant eggs are tiny objects, laid in groups free in the underground chambers and not in cells as among the bees. The eggs hatch into small white larvae which have to be taken care of by the adults. During the pupa stage a cocoon is formed which is often mistakenly called an egg; such ant "eggs" are sold as fish food.

The mouth parts of an adult ant consist of a small flap-like lip, a pair of strong-toothed mandibles, a pair of smaller maxillae and a broad lower lip. The maxillae and lower lip are provided with sensory appendages. Mandibles are the ant's hands, and are used not only in eating but in digging, carrying the young, and fighting. When eating solid food, it is first crushed and the liquid squeezed out is licked up by a roughened pad at the tip of the lower lip, which functions as a tongue. The solid residue, as well as any particles of dirt, are collected in a small pocket in the mouth, worked into a dry pellet and then cast out. No solid food enters the ant's digestive system. Ants are clean animals, constantly grooming themselves, cleaning legs and antennae by pulling them through a comb between the joints of two segments of the foreleg. Young larvae usually are fed liquids regurgitated from the mouths of the nurses.

The various stages of social life among different ants have often been compared to similar stages in the evolution of human society. Some groups, considered the most primitive, live as hunters and rely upon foraging expeditions to get their food. Such are the Army Ants, Harvester Ants, Honey Ants, and Carpenter Ants. A higher degree of social existence involves a pastoral life, keeping other insects much as we keep cattle; these are the dairymen of the ant world, of which the common Garden Ant is a good example. The most complex community has been developed by ants which have settled down to an agricultural life, growing crops and thus having a dependable supply of food close at hand. These include the Leaf-cutting Ants. A unique but not commendable way of life, which also has been practiced by man, is that found in the Slave-making and Amazon Ants.

The ARMY ANT, at home in our southern and south-western states, reaches its greatest development in the tropics. These carnivorous hunters often travel in long columns, devouring everything in their path. Even a large mammal, if tied so it cannot escape, will be completely stripped to the bone by the hungry hordes.

HARVESTER ANTS also travel in search of food, but in a less dramatic fashion. Also found in the South-west, these herbivorous ants collect seeds which they store in underground granaries. The soldier-workers, with strong mandibles, have as their job husking and breaking open the seeds for the less strong-jawed mem-

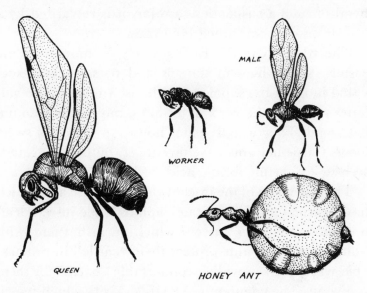

MALE

WORKER

QUEEN

HONEY ANT

Ants have elbow-like antennae and narrow waists as a result of a constriction between the thorax and abdomen. Some Honey Ant individuals (*lower right*) are used as storage jars, their abdomens distended like balloons as they are filled with the sweet liquid.

bers of the colony. Harvester Ants possess stingers, with which they can defend themselves.

Another foraging species of the Southwest is the HONEY ANT. This ant feeds on honeydew and other sweet liquids collected from plants and insects. During the season of plenty, workers store the surplus food supply in a grotesque fashion. These ants cannot construct special storage cells, as the bees do. Thus they have to use the living bodies of fellow ants as storage jars! Special ants are fed with honeydew until their crops stretch to huge proportions, and their abdomens swell into balloons. Unable to walk, these ants hang from the ceilings of their quarters. When a hungry worker strokes the head of such a suspended jam jar, it is rewarded by a few drops of regurgitated honeydew.

The BLACK CARPENTER ANT, common to the eastern states, lives in tunnels and passageways excavated in dead trees, poles, and house timbers. The galleries resemble the work of termites, but the ants do not eat wood. They usually enter houses in search of sweet foods. Carpenter ants have no stinger, but special glands secrete a smarting formic acid.

The dairymen of the insect world are those ants which have learned to "domesticate" aphids, scale insects, leafhoppers and other insects which furnish them with honeydew. Such ants protect their "cattle" in remarkable ways, even providing comfortable "barns" for them to live in. The common GARDEN ANT, which makes anthills in our gardens and cultivated fields, collects aphid eggs, feeds the young, and pastures them on corn roots. This and the other dairying species are a potential menace to farmers, since they protect and encourage the increase of insects which are injurious to our crops.

The TEXAS LEAF-CUTTING ANT, and its related species the Parasol Ants, are the farmers of the insect world. Leaf-cutting Ants live in large mounds beneath which are underground farms where thousands of industrious ants are at work. Well worn paths lead to neighboring bushes and trees, where the ants may have stripped entire plants of their leaves. The ants cut large pieces out of the leaves and, holding them erect like flags or parasols, carry them back to their mounds. In the subterranean farms the ants cut these leaves into smaller bits and pack them in spongy layers. The ants carry in their mouths also the spores of fungi, which, planted on the bed of leaves, soon form a garden of white thread-like growth. Each species of leaf-cutting ant cultivates its own kind of fungus, but most of them are related to the common field mushroom. Special workers bite the tips of the white threads and thus force clusters of small swellings, which are the food of the ants. When a new colony is formed, the beginning of its fungus garden is carried by the queen as a pellet put in her mouth, before her mating flight.

The SLAVE-MAKING ANTS do not build their own nests. When a queen starts her new colony she raids the nest of another more peaceable species, kills the queen and is accepted as queen by the "conquered" ant workers which assist the new queen in rearing her own young. To keep the colony growing, the workers raid other colonies, kill the workers and kidnap the pupae. The worker Slave-making Ants do the fighting while the slave workers do the household chores and act as nursemaids. A red species common to eastern United

States is also known as the AMAZON ANT, a suitable name for these warlike female insects.

The workers' habit of living underground has led to the loss of wings as well as of eyesight. The worker caste is much less like the queen than in the bees, and the males also are very different from the queen in appearance. Ants have retained a certain amount of freedom in their building instincts, following less rigid architectural plans. The young are reared in rooms where they can easily be picked up and removed to safety if need be. Ants are also less specialized in their feeding habits and thus less likely to be wiped out by a sudden change in their environment.

Ant workers usually are of two types. Those with large heads and powerful mandibles are the soldiers and policemen, who defend the ant colony against intruders. The smaller and less well-armed workers carry out the daily tasks in the colony, much as the worker does among the bees. Ant workers have a life span of three or four years, much greater than that of workers among other insects. In some species the queen is a huge individual, several thousand times larger than her workers. She, like the queen bee, becomes an automatic egg-laying machine whose off-spring form the entire population of the colony.

The winged queen, after the mating flight, descends to the ground and loses her wings. Her first instinctive duty is to select a suitable cavity, or excavate one, in which she seals herself up and waits for the eggs to mature in her body. The powerful wing muscles, now of no use, are absorbed and become material for the development of the eggs. When the eggs have hatched, the queen nurses the young larvae with her saliva which is not a very nourishing food; as a result the first larvae destined to become workers, or sterile females, are very small. They dig their way out into the world, forage for food for themselves and the queen. When the second brood of eggs hatch into larvae, the workers feed them more amply, so that a brood of larger workers develops. In the meantime the queen is busily laying more eggs. The increasing number of workers makes possible the building of more galleries and storerooms, the collecting of more food.

As summer progresses, some of the eggs develop into young queens, some into males. These winged forms emerge and during their flights mating takes place. The queens may start new colonies, or may return to live with their mothers—an unusual arrangement instead of the rivalry typical of bee queens. A queen ant may live for twelve to seventeen years, and the ant colony may continue in existence for thirty or forty years. If a colony gets too large, a queen with some loyal workers leaves and starts another colony nearby. The common Mound-building ant of New England has this habit. Often we find a large anthill, and near it several smaller ones. Ants from different colonies are very sociable, and make friendly visits back and forth. When the original queen dies, a succession of daughters and granddaughters carries on the egg-laying duty in the old colony.

Termites

There are two groups of termites in the United States. The WOOD TERMITES live either above or below ground, and need no connection with the earth. Their colonies are usually small. A Florida species feeds on the roots of mangrove, oak, and orange trees, and a western species has adapted itself to living in wood which may be under water. Most destructive of these is the Powderpost Termite, introduced into the Gulf states, which is rarely found outdoors. It tunnels into buildings and furniture, and even eats books and clothing.

The SUBTERRANEAN TERMITES nest in the ground, and must have their home in the earth in order to get necessary moisture. From this subterranean nest, galleries and tunnels lead to the food supply: a buried log, old stump, or fallen timber. If such wood leads into a building, the termites move on to consume timbers, floors, walls, and woodwork. Termites, undaunted by stone or metal foundations, often make runways and

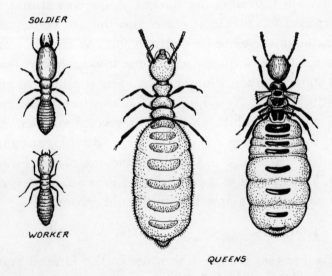

SOLDIER

WORKER

QUEENS

In the termite colony are found queens, workers and soldiers each of distinctive appearance.

– 194 –

"bridges" of mud on which they gain access to the wooden parts of a building. They may place such pathways over cement door sills, construct mud passageways inside cement blocks, between expansion joints in cement floors. Thus it is easy to understand why this termite, the common species found from Texas and Florida to Michigan and Maine, is our most harmful social insect.

The destructiveness of termites is the result of their ability to feed upon wood, a plant product which is indigestible to most insects. In the digestive system of termites, however live colonies of single-celled animals, or Protozoa, which can digest wood. The termite, in turn, feeds upon the Protozoa. This is an example of mutually beneficial living known to the biologist as symbiosis.

The social system of termites has resulted in a much more complicated caste system than among other insects. The termite community is made up of five castes, each comprising both male and female individuals. Not all these castes however occur among our American species. Heading the termite colony are the reproductives, or potential parents; these are the queens and kings. Both

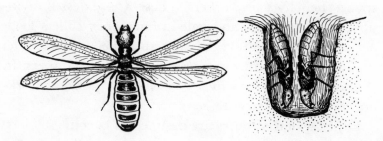

The winged male termite reveals the two pairs of wings of equal size characteristic of the group. When mating, the male and the young queen cooperate in digging the site for their future colony.

have firmer, darker bodies than the other termites; they also have wings and eyes. At certain seasons the queens and kings appear in great numbers, swarming into the air during the short period when they can fly. Swarming takes place in spring in eastern United States, in late summer in the West. After pairing off, couples settle to the ground and lose their wings. A search for a suitable nesting site then begins; when one is found, the royal pair cooperate in digging their nest which will eventually become a termite colony. This task done, the queen begins laying eggs. She may live for several years and during that period lay thousands of eggs. The king is allowed to continue as the consort of the queen, a more considerate treatment than that given to fathers in other social insects.

Another caste is made up of "stand-ins" for the royal couple. These auxiliary termites have short wings, are less darkly pigmented, and have smaller eyes. They carry on a limited amount of reproduction within the colony, and aid the queen in producing enough workers to carry on the tasks of the colony. As in other social insects, most of the eggs hatch into individuals destined to spend their lives as workers. These are sexless individuals, blind, wingless and pale in hue. They collect food, act as attendants upon the king and queen, and do the manual work of constructing tunnels and chambers. In the termite colonies which have fungus gardens, workers carry on the farm tasks.

Other sexless termites are destined to become soldiers. They are born with enlarged heads and mandibles suited for battling insect intruders into the termite colony. Some are so heavily armed that they cannot feed themselves and must be given food by the workers. The soldiers, like the workers, are blind and wingless. Their instinctive devotion to duty is unflinching, even to using their own heads in plugging up a breach in the walls of their citadel. Some soldiers are specialists in gas warfare, being equipped with a long snout through which they can shoot a sticky fluid at an enemy.

A termite colony with all these castes can be found only in the tropics. There the colony reaches mammoth size, with a million or more inhabitants and a nest of huge dimensions towering in spires with an exterior as hard as cement. Our native Subterranean Termites have no worker caste, but depend upon the child-labor of their immature young to do the work; In all termite colonies unusual care is taken of the queen. She lives in a royal chamber, and is fed such a rich diet that she becomes bed-ridden by her huge size, which may be 20,000 times the size of a worker. She lays her eggs with clock-like precision, one every few seconds; in her lifetime of ten years she may furnish the colony with 100,000,000 of her descendants!

In our insect parade, the wasps, bees, ants, and termites do not make a very impressive showing. Most of their fellow paraders are larger, or more brilliantly colored, or garbed in more striking costumes. But we know that under their drab exterior these insects have capabilities to astound us. How such behavior and devoted family attention as theirs have arisen, and how these insects know instinctively the way to carry out such complex activities, we do not know. What careful observers have learned, however, is that the social insects carry on many activities remarkably parallel to ours. Since they are present in limitless numbers at our very doorsteps, it is easy for us to find them and observe their interesting ways.

It is fitting that we should end our exploration of the insect world with the social insects. We have met many insects which as individuals arouse our admiration in their adaptations for living: the praying mantis, the carrion beetle, the seventeen-year locust, the backswimmer, the monarch and the viceroy, the Yucca moth and the silkworm moth, the bagworm, the Tachina fly. In every group of animals, individuals have body structures and habits which enable them to survive. But the social insects alone have perfected the complex way of living, with individuals specialized for certain community tasks and bearing community responsibilities. Theirs is a much older "civilization" than ours, and one patterned along very different lines. Yet it seems to be biologically very successful. Certainly the social insects provide a natural climax to life among the insects.

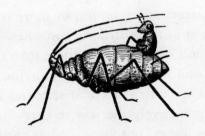

AFTERWORD

There are some kinds of animals about which so little has been written in a popular way that a beginner has difficulty in finding books which can be of help in getting to know them. This is certainly not true of insects. I doubt if any other group of animals is so well represented by available books. Some of our most popular nature writers have contributed many excellent articles and books which open the doors to an appreciation of the insect world. From this wealth of material it is difficult to select a few. However, as in preceding books in the *Young Naturalist Series,* I would like to suggest a few titles which would be a worthwhile addition to your nature library.

Field guides are essential for identifying species of insects you will find in your nature explorations. A standard guide, written by a world-famous authority on insects, is Dr. Frank E. Lutz' *Field Book of Insects,* published by G. P. Putnam's Sons. The first edition of this guide came out in 1918, and a last revision in 1948; thus it is a time-tested book. However much of it is rather detailed for the beginner, and the color plates are often inadequate. Its value lies in miscellaneous information which is interesting and the result of a lifetime of devoted study of the insects. A more recent field guide, beautifully illustrated in color, is *The Insect Guide* by Dr. Ralph B. Swain, an entomologist at the Bureau of Entomology and Plant Quarantine, U. S. Department of Agriculture. It is published by Doubleday and Company (1952). This guide is particularly valuable for the bugs and beetles, but devotes relatively little space to the butterflies and moths.

Unfortunately the two best books for use in identifying butterflies and moths are expensive and rarely available for purchase; however they can be consulted at libraries. These are *The Moth Book* by W. J. Holland, published in 1913 by Doubleday; and *The Butterfly Book,* also by W. J. Holland and published by Doubleday, in 1931. Both have a wealth of excellent color plates which make identification easy. Another useful book is *How to Know the Butterflies,* by J. H. and A. B. Comstock, published by the Comstock Publishing Company in 1936.

Collecting and preserving insects requires a knowledge of special equipment and techniques. Many museums publish guides on making insect collections. *How to Make an Insect Collection,* published by Ward's Natural Science Establishment, Rochester, N. Y. (1945) is very helpful. Also an aid to beginners is *Collection and Preservation of Insects* by P. W. Oman and A. D. Cushman, published by the U. S. Department of Agriculture as Miscellaneous Publication 601, 1946.

Of insect books written specially for young people, two are by an outstanding naturalist, Edwin Way Teale. These are *The Boys' Book of Insects,* published by Blakiston Company in 1943; and *Insect Life* published by the Boy Scouts of America in 1944. There is also the fascinating *Insect Adventures* by J. H. Fabre, published by Dodd, Mead and Company in 1929.

Apart from the identification of insects and stories of their activities, there are many books which provide information which, although written by scientists who are engaged in entomological research, can be understood by the average young naturalist. Best of these is *Insects,* The Yearbook of the Department of Agriculture for 1952. A copy can be secured from the Superintendent of Documents, Washington 25, D. C., for $2.50. This is a remarkably inexpensive yet authoritative book on various phases of insect life, especially those of economic importance to man. If you wish a textbook on entomology, the most readable and best illustrated is *An Introduction to the Study of Insects* by Borror and DeLong, of the Department of Entomology at Ohio State University. Although not a book for the beginner, if you become seriously interested in entomology you will find this text invaluable. It was published in 1954 by Rinehart and Company.

Special groups of insects, and sometimes special types, are constantly being described in articles in magazines. Three magazines contain a wealth of information on insects: *National Geographic Magazine, Nature Magazine,* and *Natural History.* If you have access to back issues of these magazines you will uncover a surprising number of articles which will help you in both identifying and understanding insects. More scientific publications on insects are published by societies of professional entomologists. The *Journal of Economic Entomology* is published by the American Association of Economic Entomologists at Menasha, Wisconsin, and the *Annals of the Entomological Society of America* is published by that society at Columbus, Ohio.

From this selected list of reference books on insects, you can see that INSECTS ON PARADE is but an eye-opener to the great amount of reading material on these animals. I hope this book has stimulated you to want to go on and read more. If so, good luck and good hunting in the insect jungles.

INDEX

Every kind of insect has a scientific name as well as a common one. The advantage of the scientific name is that there is only one for each kind of insect, and it is used throughout the world. We have discovered that many insects go by several common names, which may vary in different parts of the country. When you refer to an insect by its scientific name, however, you do not leave any doubt as to what particular insect you mean.

Every insect, like every other animal and plant, has a scientific name in two parts. The first part of the name is that of the *genus,* the second part is the *species.* For example swallowtail butterflies belong to the genus *Papilio.* But there are various kinds of swallowtails. Thus the Tiger Swallowtail has the scientific name of *Papilio glaucus;* the Spicebush Swallowtail is *Papilio troilus.* Some people call this the Green-clouded Swallowtail, so there may be confusion if you use the common names. But when you say Papilio glaucus, there is no uncertainty. Genera (the plural of genus) are grouped into families, families into orders. In the following list of species described in this book, the families are omitted and the genera and species are listed alphabetically under each order.

ORTHOPTERA. The Grasshopper Order

ODONATA. The Dragonfly Order

HEMIPTERA, Suborder HETEROPTERA: True Bugs

Kissing Bug	*Reduvius personatus*	64
Leaf Bug, Four-lined	*Poecilocapsus lineatus*	63
Planthopper	*Scolops sulcipes*	69
Squash Bug	*Anasa tristis*	61
Sycamore Lace Bug	*Corythuca ciliata*	62
Tarnished Plant Bug	*Lygus oblineatus*	62
Water Strider	*Gerris marginatus*	64
Water Boatman	*Arctocorixa interrupta*	67
Water Bug, Giant	*Lethocerus americanus*	68
Water Scorpion	*Ranatra fusca*	67

HEMIPTERA, Suborder HOMOPTERA: Bug Relatives

Aphid, Peach	*Myzus persicae*	74
Aphid, Corn-root	*Aphis maidi-radicis*	74
Blue Dodger	*Oncometopia undata*	70
Cicada, Dog-day	*Tibicen sayi*	71
Cicada; Seventeen-year Locust	*Magicicada septendecim*	71
Cochineal Insect	*Dactylopius coccus*	76
Grape Phylloxera	*Phylloxera vitifoliae*	73
Lac Insect	*Laccifer lacca*	76
Leafhopper, Red-banded	*Graphocephala coccinea*	70
Mealybug, Citrus	*Pseudococcus citri*	75
Scale, Oystershell	*Lepidosaphes ulmi*	76
Scale, San Jose	*Aspidiotus perniciosus*	76
Spittlebug	*Aphrophora quadrinotata*	70
Treehopper, Buffalo	*Ceresa bubalus*	69
Treehopper, Hickory	*Microcentrus caryae*	69

COLEOPTERA: Beetles

Asparagus Beetle	*Crioceris asparagi*	84
Apple Tree Borer, Round-headed	*Saperda candida*	82
Apple Tree Borer, Flat-headed	*Chrysobothris femorata*	82
Bombardier Beetles	*Brachinus* spp.	91
Cucumber Beetle	*Diabrotica undecimpunctata*	84
Diving Beetle	*Dytiscus marginalis*	95
Dung Beetle	*Canthon pilularius*	86
Elm Bark Beetle, European	*Scolytus multistriatus*	84
Firefly	*Photinus pyralis*	93
Fiery Searcher	*Calosoma scrutator*	91
Ground Beetle	*Pasimachus depressus*	90
Japanese Beetle	*Popillia japonica*	86
June Beetle (Junebug)	*Phyllophaga fusca*	86
Lady Beetle	*Adalia bipunctata*	92
Low-tide Billbug	*Calendra setiger*	89
Potato Beetle, Colorado	*Leptinotarsa decemlineata*	84

Powder-Post Beetle	*Lyctus opaculus*	82
Rhinoceros Beetle	*Dynastes tityus*	87
Rove Beetle, Hairy	*Creophilus maxillosus*	91
Sexton Beetle	*Necrophorus marginatus*	93
Stag Beetle	*Pseudolucanus capreolus*	87
Weevil, Boll	*Anthonomus grandis*	88
Weevil, Sweet Potato	*Cylas formicarius*	88
Whirligig Beetle	*Dineutes americanus*	96
Wireworm	*Agriotes mancus*	81

NEUROPTERA: Dobsonflies and Antlions

Antlion	*Myrmeleon immaculatus*	20
Dobsonfly; Hellgrammite	*Corydalus cornutus*	20

TRICHOPTERA: Caddisflies

Caddisfly	*Ptilostomis semifasciata*	158

LEPIDOPTERA, Suborder RHOPALOCERA: Butterflies

Cabbage Butterfly	*Pieris rapae*	114
Faun	*Grapta faunus*	111
Fritillary, Callipe	*Argynnis callipe*	121
Fritillary, Gulf	*Dione vanillae*	120
Fritillary, Great Spangled	*Argynnis cybele*	120
Fritillary, Regal	*Speyeria idalia*	120
Fritillary, Ruddy Silverspot	*Argynnis alcestis*	121
Fritillary, Silver-bordered	*Brenthis myrina*	119
Fritillary, Variegated	*Euptoieta claudia*	120
Grass-nymph	*Satyrodes canthus*	123
Hairstreak, Purple	*Atlides halesus*	124
Hairstreak, Colorado	*Hypaurotis crysalus*	125
Monarch (Milkweed)	*Danaus plexippus*	116
Mourning Cloak	*Nymphalis antiopa*	123
Purple, Banded	*Basilarchia arthemis*	124
Purple, Red-spotted	*Basilarchia astyanax*	124
Queen	*Danaus berenice*	117
Question Mark (Angle-wing)	*Polygonia interrogationis*	110
Satyr	*Grapta satyrus*	111
Sulphur, Common (Alfalfa Butterfly)	*Colias philodice*	116
Sulphur, Cloudless	*Catopsilia eubele*	116
Sulphur, Orange	*Eurymus eurytheme*	116
Swallowtail, Blue	*Papilio philenor*	109
Swallowtail, Black (Parsleyworm)	*Papilio polyxenes*	109
Swallowtail, Eastern Tiger	*Papilio glaucus*	107
Swallowtail, Giant	*Papilio cresphontes*	109

LEPIDOPTERA, Suborder HETEROCERA: Moths

Underwing, Western	*Catocala irene*	142
Webworm, Fall	*Hyphantria cunea*	141
Yucca Moth	*Tegeticula yuccasella*	135

DIPTERA: Flies and Mosquitoes

Apple Maggot	*Rhagoletis pomonella*	154
Bluebottle Fly	*Calliphora vicina*	153
Deer Fly	*Chrysops callides*	156
Flower Fly	*Lampetia equestris*	155
Hessian Fly	*Phytophaga destructor*	156
Horse Fly	*Tabanus atratus*	155
House Fly	*Mucca domestica*	153
Mediterranean Fruit Fly	*Ceratitis capitata*	154
Mexican Fruit Fly	*Anastrepha ludens*	154
Mosquito, House	*Culex pipiens*	158
Mosquito, Malaria	*Anopheles quadrimaculatus*	158
Mosquito, Salt Marsh	*Aedes sollicitans*	158
Tachina Fly	*Compsilura concinnata*	156
Vinegar Fly	*Drosophila melanogaster*	154

HYMENOPTERA: Bees, Wasps and Ants

Ant, Army	*Eciton* spp.	190
Ant, Carpenter	*Camponotus herculeanus*	190
Ant, Garden	*Lasius americanus*	190
Ant, Harvester	*Pogonomyrmex* spp.	189
Ant, Honey	*Myrmecocystus melliger*	190
Ant, Mound-building	*Formica exsectoides*	193
Ant, Texas Leaf-cutting	*Atta texana*	191
Ant, Slave-making	*Formica sanguinea*	191
Ant, Slave-making Amazon	*Polyergus lucidus*	192
Bald-faced Hornet	*Dolichovespula maculata*	172
Bumblebee	*Bombus americanorum*	175
Carpenter Bee	*Xylocopa virginica*	175
Honey Bee	*Apis mellifera*	177
Wasp, Cicada-killer	*Sphecius speciosus*	169
Wasp, Mud-dauber	*Sceliphron cementarium*	171
Wasp, Potter	*Eumenes fraternus*	170
Wasp, Sand	*Bembix spinolae*	170
Yellow-jacket	*Vespula arenaria*	171